Science and Technology Concepts for Middle Schools™

Properties of Matter

**Student
Guide
and
Source
Book**

NATIONAL SCIENCE RESOURCES CENTER

The National Science Resources Center (NSRC) is operated by the Smithsonian Institution and the National Academies to improve the teaching of science in the nation's schools. The NSRC disseminates information about exemplary teaching resources, develops curriculum materials, and conducts outreach programs of leadership development and technical assistance to help school districts implement inquiry-centered science programs.

SMITHSONIAN INSTITUTION

The Smithsonian Institution was created by act of Congress in 1846 "for the increase and diffusion of knowledge. . . ." This independent federal establishment is the world's largest museum complex and is responsible for public and scholarly activities, exhibitions, and research projects nationwide and overseas. Among the objectives of the Smithsonian is the application of its unique resources to enhance elementary and secondary education.

THE NATIONAL ACADEMIES

The National Academies are nonprofit organizations that provide independent advice to the nation on matters of science, technology, and medicine. The National Academies consist of four organizations: the National Academy of Sciences, the National Academy of Engineering, the Institute of Medicine, and the National Research Council. The National Academy of Sciences was created in 1863 by a congressional charter. Under this charter, the National Research Council was established in 1916, the National Academy of Engineering in 1964, and the Institute of Medicine in 1970.

STC/MS PROJECT SPONSORS

National Science Foundation
Bristol-Myers Squibb Foundation
Dow Chemical Company
DuPont Company
Hewlett-Packard Company
The Robert Wood Johnson Foundation
Carolina Biological Supply Company

Science and Technology Concepts for Middle Schools™

Properties of Matter

Student Guide and Source Book

National Science Resources Center

THE NATIONAL ACADEMIES • Smithsonian Institution

Published by Carolina Biological Supply Company
Burlington, North Carolina

NOTICE This material is based upon work supported by the National Science Foundation under Grant No. ESI-9618091. Any opinions, findings, and conclusions or recommendations expressed in this material are those of the authors and do not necessarily reflect views of the National Science Foundation, the Smithsonian Institution, or the National Academies.

This project was supported, in part,
by the
National Science Foundation
Opinions expressed are those of the authors
and not necessarily those of the Foundation

ISBN 978-0-89278-923-8

Published by Carolina Biological Supply Company, 2700 York Road, Burlington, NC 27215.
Call toll free 1-800-334-5551.

Cover design and illustration by Max-Karl Winkler; cover photo, Capitol Reef National Park, Utah, by David Marsland.
Printed in the United States of America

CB787680703
♻ Printed on recycled paper.

Properties of Matter

MODULE DEVELOPMENT STAFF

Developer/Writer
David Marsland

Science Advisor
Michael John Tinnesand,
Head, K-12 Science,
American Chemical Society

Editor
Kathleen Savory

Contributing Writers
Linda Harteker
Robert Taylor

Illustrator
Max-Karl Winkler

Photographic Research
Carolyn Hanson
PhotoAssist, Inc.

Design Consultation
Isely &/or Clark Design

STC/MS Project Staff

Principal Investigators
Douglas Lapp, Executive Director, NSRC
Sally Goetz Shuler, Deputy Director, NSRC

Project Director
Kitty Lou Smith

Publications Director
Heather Dittbrenner

Managing Editor
Dorothy Sawicki

Senior Editor
Linda Harteker

Illustration Coordinator
Max-Karl Winkler

Photo Editor
Janice Campion

Graphic Designer
Heidi M. Kupke

Administrative Officer
Gail Thomas

Program Assistants
Matthew Bailey
Carolyn Hanson

Publications Assistant
Famin Ahmed

STC/MS Project Advisors

Judy Barille, Chemistry Teacher, Fairfax County, Virginia, Public Schools

Steve Christiansen, Science Instructional Specialist, Montgomery County, Maryland, Public Schools

John Collette, Director of Scientific Affairs (retired), DuPont Company

Cristine Creange, Biology Teacher, Fairfax County, Virginia, Public Schools

Robert DeHaan, Professor of Physiology, Emory University Medical School

Stan Doore, Meteorologist (retired), National Oceanic and Atmospheric Administration, National Weather Service

Ann Dorr, Earth Science Teacher (retired), Fairfax County, Virginia, Public Schools; Board Member, Minerals Information Institute

Yvonne Forsberg, Physiologist, Howard Hughes Medical Center

John Gastineau, Physics Consultant, Vernier Corporation

Patricia Hagan, Science Project Specialist, Montgomery County, Maryland, Public Schools

Alfred Hall, Staff Associate, Eisenhower Regional Consortium at Appalachian Educational Laboratory

Connie Hames, Geology Teacher, Stafford County, Virginia, Public Schools

Jayne Hart, Professor of Biology, George Mason University

Michelle Kipke, Director, Forum on Adolescence, Institute of Medicine

John Layman, Professor Emeritus of Physics, University of Maryland

Thomas Liao, Professor of Engineering, State University of New York at Stony Brook

Ian MacGregor, Senior Science Advisor, Geoscience Education, National Science Foundation

Ed Mathews, Physical Science Teacher, Fairfax County, Virginia, Public Schools

Ted Maxwell, Geomorphologist, National Air and Space Museum, Smithsonian Institution

Tom O'Haver, Professor of Chemistry/Science Education, University of Maryland

Robert Ridky, Professor of Geology, University of Maryland

Mary Alice Robinson, Science Teacher, Stafford County, Virginia, Public Schools

Bob Ryan, Chief Meteorologist, WRC Channel 4, Washington, D.C.

Michael John Tinnesand, Head, K-12 Science, American Chemical Society

Grant Woodwell, Professor of Geology, Mary Washington College

Thomas Wright, Geologist (emeritus), U.S. Geological Survey; Museum of Natural History, Smithsonian Institution

Foreword

Community leaders and state and local school officials across the country are recognizing the need to implement science education programs consistent with the National Science Education Standards to attain the important national goal of scientific literacy for all students in the 21st century. The Standards present a bold vision of science education. They identify what students at various levels should know and be able to do. They also emphasize the importance of transforming the science curriculum to enable students to engage actively in scientific inquiry as a way to develop conceptual understanding as well as problem-solving skills.

The development of effective standards-based, inquiry-centered curriculum materials is a key step in achieving scientific literacy. The National Science Resources Center (NSRC) has responded to this challenge through the Science and Technology Concepts for Middle Schools (STC/MS) program. Prior to the development of these materials, there were very few science curriculum resources for middle school students that embody scientific inquiry and hands-on learning. With the publication of the STC/MS modules, schools will have a rich set of curriculum resources to fill this need.

Since its founding in 1985, the NSRC has made many significant contributions to the goal of achieving scientific literacy for all students. In addition to developing the Science and Technology for Children (STC) program—an inquiry-centered science curriculum for grades K through 6—the NSRC has been active in disseminating information on science teaching resources, in preparing school district leaders to spearhead science education reform, and in providing technical assistance to school districts. These programs have had a significant impact on science education throughout the country.

The transformation of science education is a challenging task that will continue to require the kind of strategic thinking and insistence on excellence that the NSRC has demonstrated in all of its curriculum development and outreach programs. Its sponsoring organizations, the Smithsonian Institution and the National Academies, take great pride in the publication of this exciting new science program for middle schools.

J. DENNIS O'CONNOR
Provost
Smithsonian Institution

BRUCE M. ALBERTS
President
National Academy of Sciences

Preface

The National Science Resources Center's (NSRC) mission is to improve the learning and teaching of science for K-12 students. As an organization of two prestigious scientific institutions—the National Academies and the Smithsonian Institution—the NSRC is dedicated to the establishment of effective science programs for all students. To contribute to that goal, the NSRC has developed and published two comprehensive, research-based science curriculum programs: the Science and Technology for Children® (STC®) program for students in grades K-6, and the Science and Technology Concepts for Middle Schools™ (STC/MS™) program for students in grades 6-8.

The STC/MS curriculum project was launched in 1997. The overall design of the instructional materials and the process by which they were developed are based on a foundation of research. The STC/MS courses were informed by research on cognitive development, teaching, learning, assessment, and the culture of schools.

The STC/MS curriculum materials consist of eight courses. Through these courses, students build an understanding of important concepts in life, earth, and physical sciences and in technology; learn critical-thinking skills; and develop positive attitudes toward science and technology. The STC/MS program materials are designed to meet the challenge of the National Science Education Standards to place scientific inquiry at the core of science education programs. Specifically, the National Science Education Standards state that "...students in grades 5–8 should be provided opportunities to engage in full and partial inquiries.... With an appropriate curriculum and adequate instruction, middle school students can develop the skills of investigation and the understanding that scientific inquiry is guided by knowledge, observations, ideas, and questions." STC/MS also addresses the national technology standards published by the International Technology Education Association.

Informed by research and guided by standards, the design of the STC/MS courses addresses four critical goals:

- Use of effective student and teacher assessment strategies to improve learning and teaching.
- Integration of literacy into the learning of science by giving students the lens of language to focus and clarify their thinking and activities.
- Enhanced learning using new technologies to help students visualize processes and relationships that are normally invisible or difficult to understand.
- Incorporation of strategies to actively engage parents to support the learning process.

The research and development process has included trial teaching and field-testing nationwide with geographically and ethnically diverse student populations, as well as the active involvement of the scientific and engineering communities. This process has ensured that the learning experiences contained in each module reflect current scientific thinking, and are pedagogically sound and developmentally appropriate for students.

The NSRC is grateful to the Smithsonian Institution and the National Academies for their overall project support and for sharing their scientific expertise—critical for the development of world-class products. Support for project staff and the associated work to produce and publish these materials has been made possible by the National Science Foundation, our publisher Carolina Biological Supply Company, and numerous private foundations and corporations, including Bristol-Myers Squibb Foundation, The Dow Chemical Company Foundation, DuPont, the Hewlett-Packard Company, and The Robert Wood Johnson Foundation.

The NSRC would like to acknowledge Douglas M. Lapp, former NSRC Executive Director, for his vision and leadership on the STC/MS project. The STC/MS development staff, under the direction of Kitty Lou Smith, and the publications staff, under the direction of Heather Dittbrenner, working in cooperation with Dorothy Sawicki, Managing Editor for the first four modules, and Linda Griffin Kean, Managing Editor for the second four modules, are to be commended for their creativity, dedication, and commitment to develop these excellent curriculum materials that will be used to improve the learning and teaching of middle school science in the nation's schools.

We welcome comments from students and teachers about their experiences with the STC/MS program materials and recommendations for ways the STC/MS courses can be improved.*

Sally Goetz Shuler
Executive Director
National Science Resources Center

*Please forward your feedback and suggestions to STC/MS Program, National Science Resources Center, Smithsonian Institution, Washington, DC 20560-0403.

Contents

PART 1 Characteristic Properties of Matter

Our Ideas About Matter

Matter is everywhere on Earth. What type of matter is moving these trees?

NOAA PHOTO LIBRARY/DEPARTMENT OF COMMERCE

INTRODUCTION

What is the meaning of the term "matter"? In this lesson, you will discuss the different meanings of this word and how it is used in science. You will also do a circuit of eight inquiries on the properties of matter. These inquiries are designed to get you thinking about what matter is, what its properties are, and how it behaves. The observations you make and ideas you discuss in this lesson will play a key role in the inquiries that take place later in this module.

OBJECTIVES FOR THIS LESSON

Discuss your definitions of the term "matter."

Observe some properties of matter.

Use your own words and ideas to explain these properties.

Getting Started

MATERIALS FOR
LESSON 1

1. Your teacher will place you in groups of four. What does your group think the word "matter" means? Write all the definitions you can think of on the student sheet.

2. After you have written down your definitions, your teacher will conduct a brainstorming session.

3. In this lesson, you will investigate different properties of matter. Working with another student, you will complete eight inquiries. In each inquiry, you will observe one or more properties of matter. Each pair of students will start at a different inquiry station. Your teacher will tell you at which station to begin.

4. Each inquiry has instructions you need to follow and questions you should try to answer. The procedure for each inquiry follows (see pages 4–7). It is also printed on a card placed at each station. When you make observations or think you can explain what you are observing, you should discuss these ideas with your partner. Remember: Exchanging ideas with others is a very important part of science.

5. In your own words, you will write observations, explanations, and ideas on Student Sheet 1.1.

For you
1 copy of Student Sheet 1.1: Our Ideas About Matter
1 pair of safety goggles

6. When you have completed each inquiry, put the apparatus back as you found it at the beginning of the experiment.

7. You will have only 7 minutes to do each inquiry. When your teacher calls time, you must immediately go to the next experiment in the circuit. For example, if you are at Inquiry 1.3, move to 1.4, or if you are at Inquiry 1.8A, move to 1.1A.

Inquiry 1.1
The Bottle and the Balloon

PROCEDURE

1. Hold the bottle with the balloon attached to the top in the hot pot of hot water for 2 minutes (see Figure 1.1). Answer the following question on your student sheet: What happened when you placed the bottle in the pot of hot water?

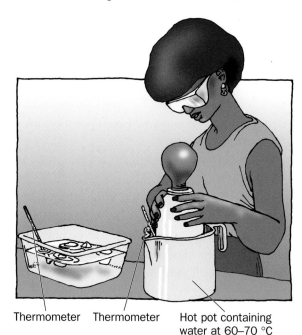

Thermometer   Thermometer   Hot pot containing water at 60–70 °C

Figure 1.1 *Place the bottle in the hot pot of hot water and hold it there for 2 minutes.*

2. Hold the bottle in the ice water for 1 minute. (If the ice has melted, you may need to add more.) Answer the following question on the student sheet: What happened when you placed the bottle in the ice water?

3. Explain your observations on the student sheet.

Inquiry 1.2
Similar Objects

PROCEDURE

1. Put exactly 50 milliliters (mL) of water into the graduated cylinder (see Figure 1.2). Record the volume of water in Table 1 on the student sheet.

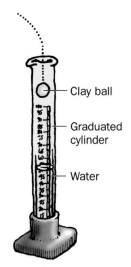

Figure 1.2 *Fill exactly half of the graduated cylinder with water. Measure and record the volume of water before adding the ball.*

— Clay ball

— Graduated cylinder

— Water

2. Put the ball into the cylinder. Avoid splashing the water.

3. Record the volume of the water and the ball in Table 1 on the student sheet.

4. Repeat the procedure using the rectangular block.

5. Use the data you have collected to calculate the volumes of the two objects. Record your results in Table 1.

6. How could you find out whether the two objects contain the same amount of matter? Write your ideas on the student sheet.

7. Return the apparatus to its original condition for the next group.

Inquiry 1.3
The Burning Candle

PROCEDURE

1. Use a match to light the candle.

2. What can you see taking place at or near the top of the candle? Write all of your observations on the student sheet.

3. Place the open end of the beaker over the candle (see Figure 1.3). Let the beaker stay over the candle for a few minutes.

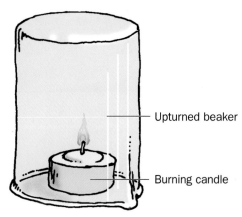

— Upturned beaker

— Burning candle

Figure 1.3 *After you have recorded your observations of the lit candle, place the beaker over the candle.*

4. What happened after the beaker was placed over the candle? Record your answer on the student sheet.

5. Why do you think the candle reacted the way it did? Write your answer on the student sheet.

6. Restore the apparatus to its original condition for the next group.

Inquiry 1.4
Describing Matter

PROCEDURE

1. Use a loupe to examine substances A and B (see Figure 1.4). Describe them on the student sheet in as much detail as possible.

Figure 1.4 *Hold the loupe close to your eye and to the substance you are examining.*

2. Answer the following question on the student sheet: Do you think either A or B is a pure substance? Justify your answer.

Inquiry 1.5
Adding Water

PROCEDURE

1. Place a clean, dry petri dish on the table in front of you.

2. Use the lab scoop to place a few grains of substance A on one side of the dish.

3. Use forceps to place a crystal of substance B on the other side of the dish.

4. Use the loupe to examine each substance. Draw a picture of what you see in Table 2 on the student sheet.

5. Use the pipette to slowly add 20 drops of water to each substance.

6. Look at the substances again using the loupe. Make a drawing of each substance on Table 2.

7. Answer the following questions on the student sheet: What happened to each substance when water was added to it? How did the two substances behave differently after water was added?

8. Place the used petri dish in the plastic box provided.

Inquiry 1.6
Mixing Liquids

PROCEDURE

1. Look at the contents of the bottle.

2. Shake the bottle two times. Allow it to stand for 2 minutes.

3. What do you observe? Write your description on the student sheet.

4. What do you know about the two substances in the bottle? Using your observations, write on the student sheet everything you know about the two substances.

Inquiry 1.7
Floating and Sinking

PROCEDURE

1. Place the squashed pan and the regular pan into the tank of water.

2. Answer the following question on the student sheet: What did you observe about each pan after it was placed in the water?

3. Both pans are made from the same substance and have the same mass. Why do the pans behave differently? Write your answer on the student sheet.

4. Remove both pans from the water and place them on the desk for the next group.

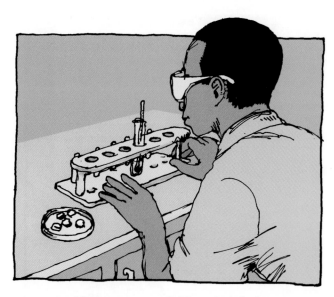

Figure 1.5 *Make sure you wait 30 seconds before you read the temperature.*

Inquiry 1.8
Reacting a Tablet

PROCEDURE

1. Fill the test tube in the test tube rack about half way with water.

2. Put the thermometer in the test tube (see Figure 1.5).

3. Wait 30 seconds and record the temperature on the student sheet.

4. Drop one piece of white tablet into the water.

5. For the next 3 minutes, carefully observe what happens.

6. What happened after the tablet was added to the water? Record your observations on the student sheet.

7. When no further changes take place, record the temperature of the water on the student sheet.

8. When you finish, empty the test tube for the next group.

REFLECTING ON WHAT YOU'VE DONE

1. When you have finished all eight inquiries, your teacher will ask your pair to return to your group.

2. Record your ideas about each experiment on the sheet of paper provided. Be prepared to contribute to a class discussion.

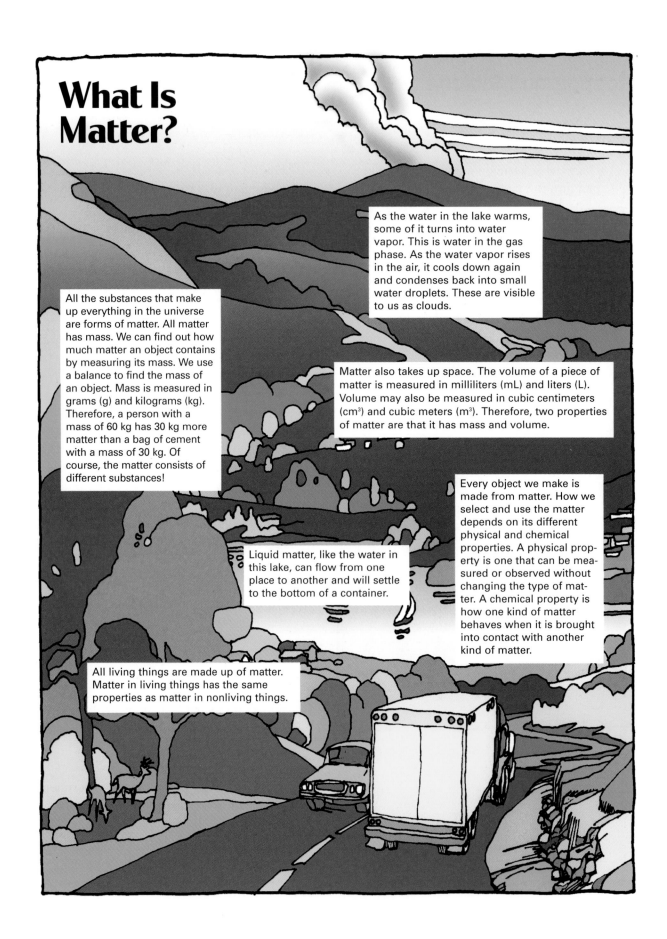

What Is Matter?

As the water in the lake warms, some of it turns into water vapor. This is water in the gas phase. As the water vapor rises in the air, it cools down again and condenses back into small water droplets. These are visible to us as clouds.

All the substances that make up everything in the universe are forms of matter. All matter has mass. We can find out how much matter an object contains by measuring its mass. We use a balance to find the mass of an object. Mass is measured in grams (g) and kilograms (kg). Therefore, a person with a mass of 60 kg has 30 kg more matter than a bag of cement with a mass of 30 kg. Of course, the matter consists of different substances!

Matter also takes up space. The volume of a piece of matter is measured in milliliters (mL) and liters (L). Volume may also be measured in cubic centimeters (cm^3) and cubic meters (m^3). Therefore, two properties of matter are that it has mass and volume.

Every object we make is made from matter. How we select and use the matter depends on its different physical and chemical properties. A physical property is one that can be measured or observed without changing the type of matter. A chemical property is how one kind of matter behaves when it is brought into contact with another kind of matter.

Liquid matter, like the water in this lake, can flow from one place to another and will settle to the bottom of a container.

All living things are made up of matter. Matter in living things has the same properties as matter in nonliving things.

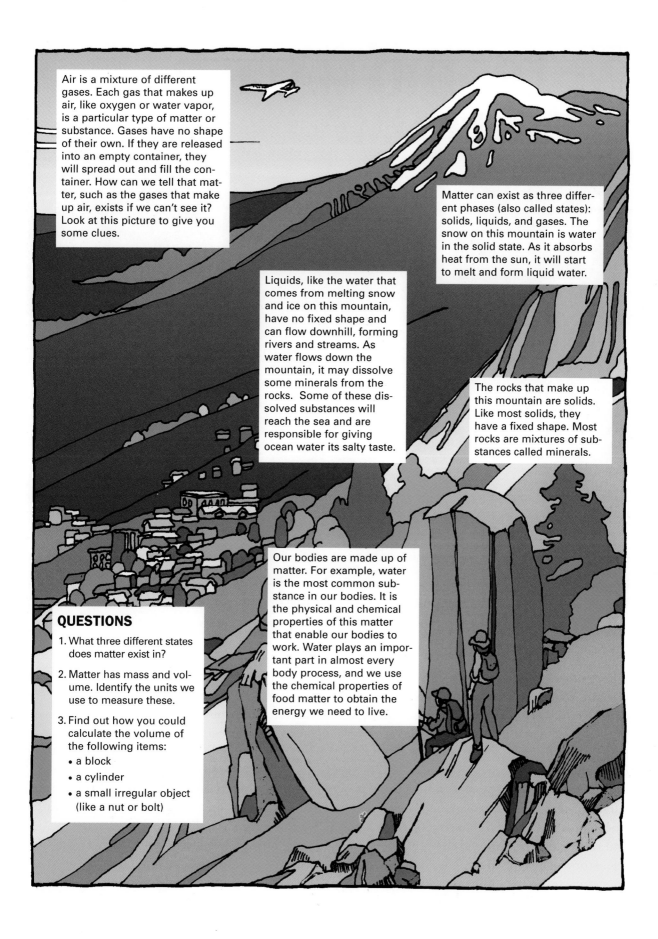

Air is a mixture of different gases. Each gas that makes up air, like oxygen or water vapor, is a particular type of matter or substance. Gases have no shape of their own. If they are released into an empty container, they will spread out and fill the container. How can we tell that matter, such as the gases that make up air, exists if we can't see it? Look at this picture to give you some clues.

Matter can exist as three different phases (also called states): solids, liquids, and gases. The snow on this mountain is water in the solid state. As it absorbs heat from the sun, it will start to melt and form liquid water.

Liquids, like the water that comes from melting snow and ice on this mountain, have no fixed shape and can flow downhill, forming rivers and streams. As water flows down the mountain, it may dissolve some minerals from the rocks. Some of these dissolved substances will reach the sea and are responsible for giving ocean water its salty taste.

The rocks that make up this mountain are solids. Like most solids, they have a fixed shape. Most rocks are mixtures of substances called minerals.

Our bodies are made up of matter. For example, water is the most common substance in our bodies. It is the physical and chemical properties of this matter that enable our bodies to work. Water plays an important part in almost every body process, and we use the chemical properties of food matter to obtain the energy we need to live.

QUESTIONS

1. What three different states does matter exist in?

2. Matter has mass and volume. Identify the units we use to measure these.

3. Find out how you could calculate the volume of the following items:
   - a block
   - a cylinder
   - a small irregular object (like a nut or bolt)

WHERE DID MATTER COME FROM?

These Australian Aborigines are painting images of their Dreamtime story.

Where did all the stuff in the universe—Earth, the sun, rocks, plants, animals, even you—come from? Was it made at a certain time? If so, how long has it been around? Has it always been there? People have asked these questions since the earliest times.

Most cultures have stories of how the universe was created. For instance, Australian Aborigines tell a story about the sun, moon, and stars sleeping beneath the ground. Their ancestors also slept there. One day the ancestors woke up and came to the surface. The Aborigines call this the Dreamtime.

During the Dreamtime, the ancestors walked the Earth as animals such as kangaroos, lizards, and wombats. Out of beings that were half animal and half plant, the ancestors made people. They then went back to sleep. Some went underground, but some became objects such as trees and rocks. The Dreamtime is an important part of Australian Aboriginal culture.

Scientists have also tried to answer the question of how the universe began. When scientists try to answer questions, they sometimes make observations of what happens and

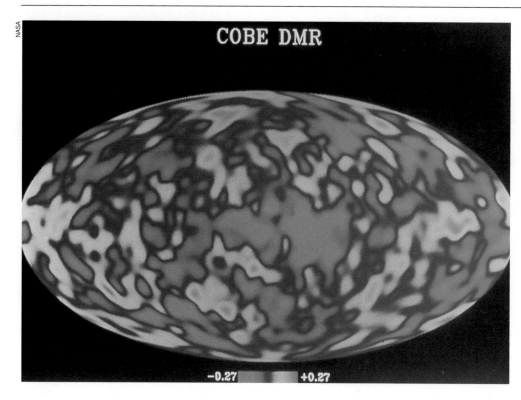

This background radiation map of the universe was produced using data collected by COBE (see photo below). The purple spots represent energy at the farthest edges of the expanding universe, giving a "picture" of the universe about 1 million years after the Big Bang. This image shows that even then, "structures" were being formed.

collect data. Scientists use their observations and data to try to explain the phenomena they are studying. One important part of science is the ability for different scientists to make the same observations and collect the same data when they are studying the same phenomena. When many scientists have made the same observations over a period of time, their explanations of these observations are called theories. As new knowledge is gained, theories are tested and retested. Sometimes the theories don't stand up to the new information. These theories are then replaced with new theories.

Over the years, as scientists have gained new knowledge about the universe, new theories have replaced old theories. Currently, many scientists think the universe started with the "Big Bang." The Big Bang theory suggests that all the matter and energy in the universe exploded out from one point. As the explosion occurred, energy and matter spread outward and formed the universe. The

The Cosmic Background Explorer (COBE) satellite was launched in 1989. Its mission: Find out more about the origins of the universe by looking for background radiation left over from the Big Bang.

matter from the Big Bang formed clouds of gas. As these gases cooled and condensed, stars, galaxies, and eventually planets and other "structures" that make up the universe were formed.

Even now, billions of years after the Big Bang, the universe is still spreading out. By looking at light from distant stars and galaxies, scientists can observe and measure this expansion. Using special apparatus, they can also detect some of the background glow of invisible energy left over from the Big Bang.

Space telescopes, such as the Hubble telescope and X-ray telescopes in orbit around Earth, are constantly making new and exciting observations. Ideas about the formation of the universe and the Big Bang may change as these instruments are used to discover more about our evolving universe. □

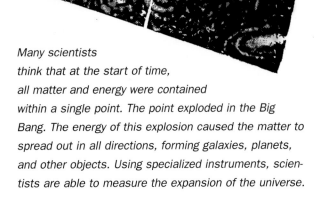

Many scientists think that at the start of time, all matter and energy were contained within a single point. The point exploded in the Big Bang. The energy of this explosion caused the matter to spread out in all directions, forming galaxies, planets, and other objects. Using specialized instruments, scientists are able to measure the expansion of the universe.

QUESTIONS

1. Use information from this reader and any other information you can find from books, CD-ROMs, or the Internet to list the evidence for the Big Bang theory.

2. In science, the term "theory" has a special meaning. Find a definition of this term and give two examples of other theories that are used in physical science.

Determining Density

CORBIS/DIGITAL STOCK

How can this diver remain at this depth? Why doesn't he float to the surface or sink to the bottom of the sea?

INTRODUCTION

In this lesson, you will start to investigate a property of matter called density. To do this, you will have to measure the mass and volume of several different objects made from different substances. You will then use the data you have collected to determine the mass of 1.0 cubic centimeter of the substance from which the objects are made.

OBJECTIVES FOR THIS LESSON

Discuss the terms "mass" and "volume."

Find the mass of a known volume of water.

Calculate the mass of 1.0 cubic centimeter of water.

Measure the mass and volume of some regular and irregular objects.

Calculate the density of these objects.

Getting Started

1. In your notebook, write what you think the difference is between mass and volume. After a few minutes, your teacher will lead a class discussion on mass and volume. Be prepared to contribute your ideas to this discussion.

2. After the discussion, write your own definitions for mass and volume in your science notebook. Include the units you would use for measuring each of them.

3. Read "Useful Calculations" on page 16.

MATERIALS FOR LESSON 2

For you

1 copy of Student Sheet 2.1: Measuring the Mass and Volume of Water

1 copy of Student Sheet 2.2: Comparing the Densities of Different Substances

1 copy of Student Sheet 2.3: Measuring the Densities of Irregular Objects

For your group

2 100-milliliter (mL) graduated cylinders

1 aluminum block

1 transparent plastic block

1 wax block

1 white plastic block

Metric rulers

1 copper cylinder

1 nylon spacer

1 steel bolt

Paper towels or newspaper

Access to an electronic balance

Calculators, if available

USEFUL CALCULATIONS

Volume is a measure of space taken up by some matter. In this module, the units cubic centimeters or milliliters are used when measuring volume. Because 1 milliliter equals 1 cubic centimeter, these units are interchangeable.

The volume that something takes up can be measured in several different ways. A graduated cylinder can be used to measure the volume of liquids. The exterior dimensions of regular solid objects can be measured to calculate their volume. For example, the volume (measured in cubic centimeters) of a block can be calculated by measuring the block's length (l), height (h), and width (w) in centimeters and then multiplying these together, as shown in the following equation:

Volume of a block =
l (centimeter) × h (centimeter) ×
w (centimeter) = volume in cubic centimeters

Different formulas can be used to calculate the volume of other regular objects (such as cylinders or spheres). Volumes of solids can also be measured indirectly by using a graduated cylinder. This method is done by the displacement of water. You used this method in Inquiry 1.2.

Mass is a measure of the amount of matter in an object. In this module, gram is used as the unit for measuring mass. Mass can be measured using a balance.

The density of a substance is the mass of a known volume of a substance. It is usually measured in grams per cubic centimeter.

Inquiry 2.1
Measuring the Mass and Volume of Water

PROCEDURE

1. Collect the plastic box of materials for your group. Check its contents against the materials list. During this lesson, you will also use an electronic balance. Other groups will be sharing the balance with you. Your teacher will assign an electronic balance to your group.

2. Work with your partner. Take one of the graduated cylinders out of the plastic box. Examine it carefully. Discuss the answers to the following questions with your partner:

A. What is the unit of measure for the graduated cylinder?

B. What is the maximum volume it can measure?

C. What is the minimum volume it can measure?

D. What is the number of units measured by the smallest division on its scale?

3. In this experiment, you will investigate the mass of different volumes of a substance. The substance you will use is water. Discuss with your partner how you could find the mass of 50 mL of water by using the graduated cylinder and the electronic balance. Consider the measurements and the calculations you need to make. Write your ideas in your notebook. You will be expected to contribute your ideas to a short class discussion.

4. Record the steps of the agreed-upon class procedure on Student Sheet 2.1.

5. Make sure that before you place anything on the balance it reads 0.0 gram (g) (see Figure 2.1). If the balance does not read 0.0 g, press the button marked ZERO. Wait for 0.0 g to appear before continuing. Once you place an object on the balance, wait a few seconds for the reading to stabilize before recording your measurement.

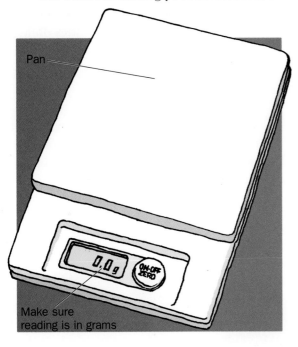

Pan

0.0 g   ON-OFF ZERO

Make sure reading is in grams

Figure 2.1 *Make sure the balance reads 0.0 g before placing an object on it.*

6. Look at Figure 2.2 to review how to accurately measure volume with a graduated cylinder.

7. Follow the class procedure to find the mass of 50 mL of water. Record your measurements in Table 1 on the student sheet.

8. Complete the last column of Table 1. You can calculate the mass of 1 cm³ of water by dividing the mass of the water by the volume of the water.

9. Repeat the experiment using 25 mL of water. Remember, you already know the mass of the graduated cylinder.

10. Use your results to answer the following questions on Student Sheet 2.1: Does changing the volume of water change the mass of 1 cm³ of water? Does changing the mass of water change the mass of 1 cm³ of water? What is the density of water in grams per cubic centimeter (g/cm³)? Does changing the mass or volume of water change its density?

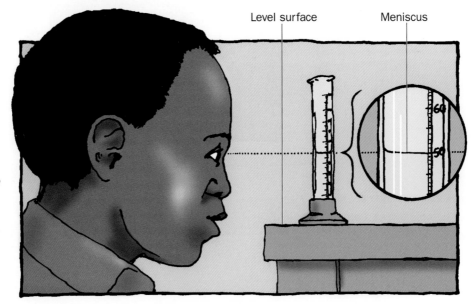

Level surface   Meniscus

60

50

Figure 2.2 *Make sure the graduated cylinder is on a level surface. When you take a reading, make sure your eye is level with the bottom of the meniscus. The "meniscus" is the curved upper surface of the water in the cylinder.*

Inquiry 2.2
Comparing the Densities of Different Substances

PROCEDURE

1. Take the blocks of wax, transparent plastic, white plastic, and aluminum (the silver-colored metal) out of the plastic box.

2. Discuss the following questions with the other members of your group:

A. Do you think all of these blocks have the same density?

B. What evidence do you have to support your answer?

C. What measurements will you need to make to test your hypothesis?

3. Work with your partner to determine the density of each of the blocks (see Figure 2.3). You will need to share the blocks with the other members of your group. Record your results in Table 1 on Student Sheet 2.2.

4. Check your results and calculations against those of the other pair in your group. If your calculated densities do not match (to within 0.1 g/cm³), repeat your calculations.

5. Answer the following questions on the student sheet: Are the densities of the different substances the same or different? How could this information be used to identify the substance from which an object is made?

Figure 2.3 *Use the ruler to measure the blocks. Calculate the volume of each block in cubic centimeters. Use the balance to measure the mass of the blocks.*

Inquiry 2.3
Measuring the Densities of Irregular Objects

PROCEDURE

1. In this inquiry, you will determine the density of some objects with complex shapes. Remove the three objects (steel bolt, copper cylinder, and nylon spacer) from the plastic box.

2. Discuss with other members of your group how you could find the density of each of these objects. Refer to Inquiry 1.2 for help in finding the volume of objects. You will discuss your ideas with the rest of the class before proceeding with the inquiry.

3. Draw a series of simple diagrams in the boxes on Student Sheet 2.3, showing how you are going to find out the mass and volume of the objects. You may not need to use all the boxes.

4. Work with your partner to devise a table in which to record your data. You may

need to make some rough layouts in your notebook. Make sure you include space in the table for all your measurements, your calculations, and the density of the objects. Use the correct units of measure when labeling columns. When you have decided on a good layout, use a ruler to draw your table in the space provided on Student Sheet 2.3.

5. Find the mass, volume, and density for each of the objects. Both pairs in your group should find the mass of each of the objects *before* immersing them in water. Check your results with the other pair in your group. You can ignore small differences in the densities you have obtained.

6. Complete your data table.

7. Answer the following questions on Student Sheet 2.3: Are any of the blocks from Inquiry 2.2 or objects from this inquiry made from the same substance? How did you reach your conclusion? How do the densities of the objects compare with the density of water?

REFLECTING ON WHAT YOU'VE DONE

1. During the lesson, you measured the mass and volume and calculated the density of a liquid and some solids. All the substances had different densities. Your teacher will lead a discussion about the results from all three inquiries. To help you participate in the discussion, write your answers to the following questions in your notebook:

A. *What is the difference between mass and volume?*

B. *What units did you use to measure mass and volume?*

C. *How did you calculate the density of an object?*

D. *What units did you use to measure density?*

E. *Does changing the amount of a substance change its density?*

F. *If two objects are made from the same substance, will they have the same density?*

2. Read "Density as a Characteristic Property."

DENSITY AS A CHARACTERISTIC PROPERTY

The density of a substance is a characteristic of that substance. Therefore, density is a property that can be used to help identify a substance. Properties used to help identify substances are called characteristic properties.

Characteristic properties are not affected by the amount or shape of a substance: A bolt made from iron will have the same characteristic properties as the hull of an iron ship or a piece of iron railing. You will encounter more characteristic properties later in the module. Perhaps you can think of some now.

Knowing the density of a substance can be useful. For example, substances with low densities can be used to make objects that fly. Based on the results you obtained in Lesson 2, do you think steel or aluminum would be better for building an airplane? Would you want to make a bike out of lead? Why or why not?

Mass or Weight?

What is the weight of the sugar inside the bag in the picture? If you answer the question by saying 1 kilogram, you would be wrong! You see, kilograms and grams are units of mass, not weight. Weight is measured in units called newtons. Confused by the difference between mass and weight? Why do we need different units?

We have already discussed that mass is a measure of the amount of matter in an object. The bag contains sugar with a mass of 1 kilogram. Weight is quite different from mass. It is a measure of the force

of gravity. Gravity is the force of attraction between two objects. Earth and the sugar are attracted to each other. This attraction varies with the size of the two objects and their distance apart. The force of attraction between a mass of 1 kilogram and Earth is about 9.8 newtons. So the answer to the question "How much does the sugar in this bag weigh?" is 9.8 newtons.

If an astronaut took the bag of sugar to the moon, what would be its mass? Would it contain the same amount of matter? The answer is yes. Provided the

How much does this bag of sugar weigh?

astronaut hasn't eaten or dropped any of the sugar, the bag would still contain sugar with a mass of 1 kilogram. What is the weight of the bag of sugar on the moon? The moon is much smaller than Earth, so the force of attraction between the sugar and the moon is less. Gravity on the moon is about

one-sixth of that on Earth. So what is the weight of sugar on the moon? Divide 9.8 newtons by 6 and you'll get an approximate answer. □

QUESTION

How would the weight of the same bag of sugar on Mars and Jupiter differ from that on Earth? Explain your answer.

When it comes to mass, it doesn't matter where you are because the mass of an object is always the same. But if you are buying something by weight, you will get a lot more for the same cost if you buy it on the moon!

Archimedes' Crowning Moment

Archimedes, one of the most famous mathematicians and scientists of ancient Greece, had a problem. The king had a new crown. It looked like pure gold. But the king was suspicious. How could he be sure that the jeweler hadn't cheated him by adding another, less valuable metal to the molten gold? The king asked Archimedes to find out whether the crown was made from pure gold.

Archimedes knew his reputation was on the line. He could have taken

COURTESY OF THE SMITHSONIAN INSTITUTION, NEG. #56119

Archimedes was an expert on mass, volume, and density.

the problem down to the public marketplace, where he often went to discuss scientific questions with other scholars. But instead, he decided to relax in a bath. The tub was filled to the brim. Still concentrating on his problem, Archimedes immersed himself in the water.

Splash! Water spilled over the sides of the tub and onto the floor. He had made a real mess. But that mess triggered an idea—an idea that would help solve the king's dilemma.

"When I got into the tub," Archimedes reasoned, "my body displaced a lot of water. Now, there must be a relationship between my volume and the volume of water that my body displaced—because if I weren't so big, less water would have spilled on my floor."

This observation brought Archimedes back to the problem of the gold crown. What if he put it in water? How much water would it displace? And could he apply this observation to prove that the crown was made of pure gold?

Archimedes knew about the importance of controls, so he began by finding a piece of gold and a piece of silver with

"Hmmm . . . the volume of my body equals the volume of water on the bathroom floor."

exactly the same mass. He dropped the gold into a bowl filled to the brim with water and measured the volume of water that spilled out. Then he did the same thing with the piece of silver.

Although both metals had the same mass, the silver had a larger volume; therefore, it displaced more water than did the gold. That's because the silver was less dense than gold.

Now it was time to check out the crown. Archimedes found a piece of pure gold that had the same mass as the crown. He placed the pure gold chunk and the crown in water, one at a time.

The crown displaced more water than the piece of gold. Therefore, its density was less than pure gold. The king had been cheated! Although this was just one of Archimedes' many contributions to science, there's no doubt that it was his "crowning moment"! ☐

QUESTION

Pretend you are Archimedes. What instructions would you give for comparing the density of a crown with the density of gold?

Density Predictions

How could your knowledge of density be used to help clean up this oil spill?

INTRODUCTION

Why is it useful to know about density? You have already discussed how density, because it is a characteristic property of matter, can be used as one way to help identify a substance. You can also use the density of an object or substance to predict how it may behave under different conditions. For example, have you ever done experiments that involved investigating whether objects float or sink in water? Apart from guessing, how can you tell whether an object will float or sink? Are there some measurements that can be used to predict floating and sinking? In this lesson, you will use the data you have already collected on density and relate it to floating and sinking. You will then use density to predict how solids and liquids behave in a density column.

OBJECTIVES FOR THIS LESSON

Predict whether an object will float or sink on the basis of how it feels.

Use density to predict whether a substance will float or sink in water.

Determine the density of different liquids.

Build a density column.

Use density to predict how solids will behave when they are placed in a density column.

Getting Started

1. Collect the plastic box of materials for your group. Check its contents against the materials list. During this lesson, you will use an electronic balance. Your teacher will assign an electronic balance to your group. Other groups will be sharing the balance with you.

2. Take the blocks of aluminum, wax, and white and transparent plastic out of the plastic box. As a group, predict whether each object will float or sink in water and explain how you reached your prediction.

3. Your teacher will list the predictions for each group and may ask you to explain your predictions to the rest of the class.

4. Your teacher will ask some of you to test your predictions. Use the results of these tests and the data you collected in Lesson 2 to fill in Table 1 on Student Sheet 3.1.

5. Answer the following question on the student sheet: Is there a relationship between density and floating and sinking in water? If so, describe what this relationship is.

MATERIALS FOR LESSON 3

For you
- 1 copy of Student Sheet 3.1: Using Density To Make Predictions
- 1 copy of Student Sheet 3: Homework for Lesson 3

For you and your lab partner
- 2 100-mL graduated cylinders
- 1 250-mL beaker containing colored water
- 1 copper cylinder
- 1 nylon spacer
- 1 test tube brush

For your group
- 1 aluminum block
- 1 transparent plastic block
- 1 wax block
- 1 white plastic block
- 1 bottle of vegetable oil
- 1 bottle of corn syrup

For the class
- Access to an electronic balance
- Access to water
- 1 container for collecting vegetable oil waste
- 1 container for collecting corn syrup and water waste
- Paper towels
- Detergent

Inquiry 3.1
Building a Density Column

PROCEDURE

1. In this inquiry, you will work in pairs and share the bottles of oil and syrup with other members of your group.

2. Look carefully at Table 2 on Student Sheet 3.1. You need to determine the density of three liquids. You already have some of this information.

3. Spend a few minutes carefully reviewing the procedure you used in Inquiry 2.1 to determine the density of water.

4. Use the same procedure to find out the density of corn syrup and vegetable oil. Use 25 mL of each substance. Use a different graduated cylinder for each substance. The graduated cylinders may have different masses. Be sure to check the mass of each. *Do not empty the cylinders; you will need both of the liquids later in this inquiry.*

5. Use the data you collected to fill in Table 2 on Student Sheet 3.1.

6. Look carefully at the densities you have calculated. Answer the following question on the student sheet: What do you predict will happen when you mix together the vegetable oil, corn syrup, and water? Explain your prediction. Fill in the diagram of the prediction cylinder on the student sheet.

7. Pour the 25 mL of vegetable oil into the cylinder containing the corn syrup. Add an additional 25 mL of colored water from the beaker. (The colored water has the same density as water.) Allow the contents of the cylinder to settle.

8. Fill in and label the diagram of the observation cylinder on the student sheet.

9. Answer the following questions on the student sheet: Do the liquids mix together (miscible) or form distinct layers (immiscible)? What is the relationship between the density of the liquid and its position in the graduated cylinder?

10. Use information you obtained in Inquiry 2.1 to predict what will happen when you drop the copper cylinder into your density column and when you drop the nylon spacer into the column. Discuss your ideas with your partner.

11. Drop the copper cylinder, followed by the nylon spacer, into the column. Observe what happens. Record your results in the diagram of the observation cylinder on the student sheet. Label each object and write down its density.

12. Carefully pour the vegetable oil into the container provided for this purpose; do the same with the syrup and water.

13. Using the test tube brush, thoroughly wash all the graduated cylinders and objects in a detergent solution.

14. Dry the objects with a paper towel. Stand the graduated cylinders upside down in a sink or on newspaper to allow them to drain.

15. If you have spilled any substances, wipe off your table.

REFLECTING ON WHAT YOU'VE DONE

1. Write a short paragraph in your science notebook explaining your observations. Make sure you include the words "density" and "immiscible" in your description. Be prepared to read your paragraph to the rest of the class.

2. Your teacher will show the bottle containing two liquids that you used in Inquiry 1.6. Use your knowledge of immiscible liquids and density to explain (in your notebook) the appearance and behavior of the liquids in the bottle.

3. Oil is less dense than water. Discuss with other members of your group how this information can be applied to cleaning up a spill from an oil tanker.

Why Did the *Titanic* Float?

On April 10, 1912, the luxury liner *Titanic* left England for New York and sailed straight into the annals of history. Why is the name *Titanic* so well known? At that time, she was considered the safest ship ever built; some people even considered her unsinkable. The *Titanic* became famous when she struck an iceberg and sank on her first voyage. About 1500 people drowned or froze to death in the ice-cold Atlantic water.

People often ask, "Why did the *Titanic* sink?" Perhaps a better question would be, "Why did the ship float?" She was, after all, made mainly from iron and steel. Her anchors alone weighed 28 metric

This newspaper article reported on the disastrous maiden voyage of the Titanic. *Why was this voyage a disaster? What role did density play in the tragedy?*

tons. (That's almost 62,000 pounds!) Steel has a density about eight times that of water, so you would expect a ship made of steel to sink.

However, if you were to look at a plan of the *Titanic*, you would discover that most of her volume was occupied by air. Air has a density of about one-thousandth that of water. Therefore, the average density of the ship was less than the density of water. That's why she floated.

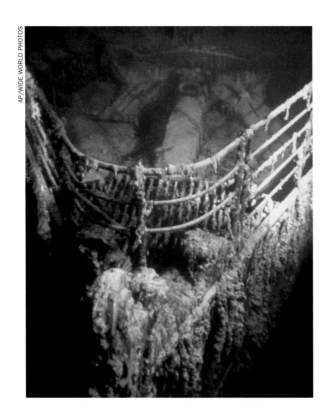

The Titanic *now lies under 12,500 feet of water. It was made mainly from steel, which is denser than water. How did it manage to float at all?*

Icebergs float in water. What does this tell us about their density?

Why did she sink? When the *Titanic* hit the iceberg, water rushed into the ship's hull and displaced the air. The average density of the water and the steel ship was greater than the density of water. The result of this change? The *Titanic* sank to the bottom of the Atlantic. ☐

QUESTIONS

Unfortunately, life vests, or personal flotation devices (PFDs), were not enough to save the lives of many of the *Titanic's* passengers. However, they save hundreds of lives every year.

1. If you were designing a PFD, what factors would you need to take into account?
2. Draw a diagram of a PFD of your own design. Label it, explaining the role of each of its parts, and be sure to include the word "density" somewhere in your explanation.

4

Do Gases Have Density?

SCIENCE VU/VISUALS UNLIMITED

*A destructive tornado like this one
is evidence that air is matter.*

INTRODUCTION

Have you ever thought about air? Air is strange
stuff. It's invisible, yet we know it exists. We can
feel our own breath or see the effect of the
wind. But is air matter? If it is, then it must
have both mass and volume. In this lesson, you
will find out whether air has mass and volume.

OBJECTIVES FOR THIS LESSON

Find out whether air has volume.

Design an experiment that can be used
to find out the mass of a sample of air.

Try to measure the mass of a sample
of air.

Discuss the accuracy of the procedure.

Getting Started

1. Your teacher will show you two pieces of apparatus. In the first one, the funnel goes into the test tube but is held firmly in place by a rubber stopper. The second test tube also holds a funnel but is not sealed around the edge of the tube.

2. In your science notebook, describe what happens when colored water is poured into each funnel (see Figure 4.1). Try to explain why water behaves differently in each funnel.

MATERIALS FOR LESSON 4

For you
  1 copy of Student Sheet 4.1: Finding the Density of Air

For your group
  1 thick-walled plastic bottle
  1 rubber washer
  1 vacuum pump with vacuum stopper (rubber valve)
  1 100-mL graduated cylinder
     Access to water
     Access to an electronic balance

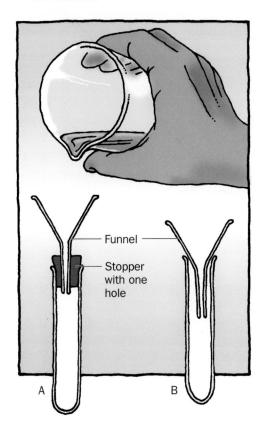

Funnel

Stopper with one hole

A   B

Figure 4.1 *In this experiment, colored water is poured into both funnels.*

3. Your teacher will pass around the second piece of apparatus, which consists of two syringes connected by a tube.

4. Try to explain what you observe when one syringe is pushed in. In your note-

book, draw what happens when the syringe is pushed in (see Figure 4.2).

5. What do these two experiments tell you about air? Write your answer in your notebook.

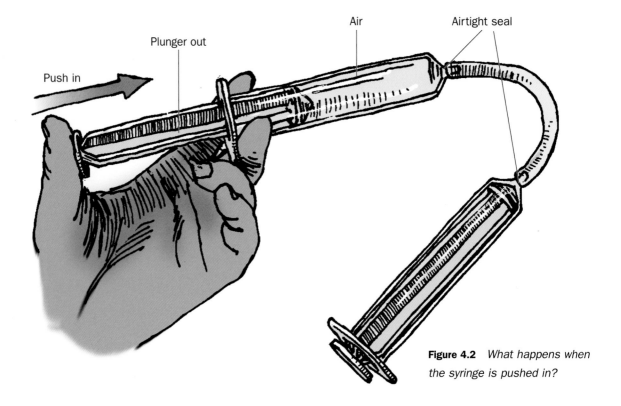

Figure 4.2 *What happens when the syringe is pushed in?*

Inquiry 4.1
Finding the Density of Air

PROCEDURE

1. What will you need to measure in order to calculate the density of air? Examine the contents of your plastic box and try to think how you could use the apparatus and an electronic balance to find the density of some air (see Figure 4.3). Discuss your ideas with the rest of your group. Try to agree on a procedure that you think will work. Write down your ideas in a short paragraph in your notebook. Be prepared to present your group's ideas to the rest of the class.

2. After all the groups have shared their ideas, your teacher will use them to devise a standard procedure. Record the procedure on Student Sheet 4.1.

3. Use the procedure to find the mass and volume of an air sample. Under Steps 2 and 3 on the student sheet, record your results and use them to calculate the density of air.

4. Return the apparatus to your plastic box.

REFLECTING ON WHAT YOU'VE DONE

1. Your teacher will write down the different group results for this experiment. Look carefully at the results. Answer the following question on the student sheet: How does the density of air compare with the density of solids and liquids?

2. Are the results all the same? Do you think the procedure you used is very precise? Answer the following question on the student sheet: Why do the class results vary so much?

3. You have discovered that air does have density. Use this information to answer the following question on the student sheet: Why do some things float in air?

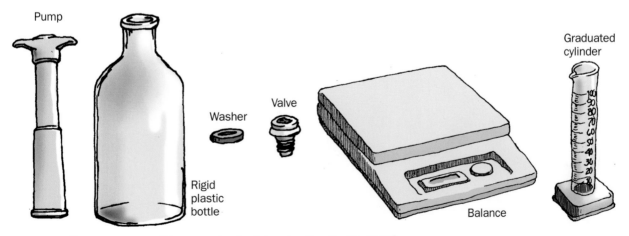

Pump   Washer   Valve   Rigid plastic bottle   Balance   Graduated cylinder

Figure 4.3   *How can you use this apparatus to determine the density of air?*

DEADLY DENSITY

Have you heard about a substance called chlorine? If you have, you probably know that it is sometimes added to water. Chlorine is added to drinking water to kill harmful microorganisms. When you go swimming, you can smell the chlorine at the pool. That's because chemicals that release chlorine are added to the water to keep it safe for swimming.

You may be surprised to learn that chlorine is a greenish yellow gas. It is also a very poisonous substance. This property is exploited when chlorine is used as a disinfectant to kill microorganisms. In small amounts, chlorine kills microbes but not larger organisms. However, chlorine has also been used to kill people.

In World War I (1914–1918), chlorine was used as a weapon. Most of the battles in this war were fought between lines of trenches that provided the soldiers with some protection against gunfire. On April 22, 1915, at the battle of Ypres, in France, the Germans used a new

Chlorine is used to kill the microorganisms in swimming pools.

secret weapon. That weapon was chlorine. They released chlorine gas from their side of the lines. The chlorine was carried by the wind to the enemy trenches. Because chlorine is much denser than air, it stayed near the ground and poured into the trenches. Choked and blinded, the defenders were then overrun by German troops wearing gas masks. After this gas attack, soldiers on both sides were issued gas masks. ☐

QUESTION

What are other properties and uses of chlorine? Use the library and Internet resources to find out more about chlorine.

To protect themselves against poisonous gases in World War I, these U.S. troops and their mules wore gas masks.

AIR HEADS

What do a scuba diver and an astronaut have in common? They both have air on their minds. Air is something most of us take for granted. We might think about it when we are swimming or exercising, but otherwise we know there is plenty of it around. The air that surrounds our entire planet is called the atmosphere. To an astronaut and a diver, air is something to think about. They have to carry an atmosphere with them: their own supply of air compressed into a small tank. If it runs out, they are in big trouble!

Why do we need air? Sometimes people say, "We need air to breathe." This is the opposite of the truth. In fact, we breathe because we need air—even then, we only need part of it. Air is a mixture of gases. The part we use is called oxygen, and it makes up about one-fifth of normal atmospheric air.

Why is oxygen so important? Our bodies use oxygen to combine with food substances in a process called respiration. Respiration releases energy that we can then use for our body processes (another gas, carbon dioxide, also found in air, is made in this process). If you were deprived of oxygen for more than a few minutes, these life processes would stop. You would suffocate to death!

Oxygen is also needed for things to burn. Think back to what happened in Lesson 1 when you placed a beaker over a burning candle. The candle went out because it had used up most of the oxygen in the air. Things burn very quickly in pure oxygen. In fact, burning things in pure oxygen can be explosive. It's a good thing that air consists mainly of another gas called nitrogen.

From our point of view, nitrogen gas doesn't do very

What do these two explorers have on their minds?

COURTESY OF NASA/PHOTOASSIST, INC.

A layer of air called the atmosphere surrounds Earth.

© TOM J. ULRICH/VISUALS UNLIMITED

This fierce forest fire would burn explosively if the atmosphere were pure oxygen. Luckily, air consists mainly of less reactive nitrogen.

much. Our bodies don't use it, very few substances react with it, and it's colorless and odorless. Many of the other gases found in air don't do much either. Some of these gases, including argon, neon, and helium, are so renowned for doing nothing that they are called inert gases.

Other gases are more important to living things. Without the 0.03 percent of carbon dioxide in the air, there would be no green plants. Plants use carbon dioxide to make food. They use the energy from sunlight to combine water with carbon dioxide to make carbohydrates. They turn parts of the air into living matter! Most plants absorb water through their roots, but water is also found in the air (it's called water vapor). The amount of water in the form of water vapor varies. On hot, sticky days, you can easily feel that there's a lot of water in the air.

There are other gases in air. Some of these occur naturally;

This leaf is a factory that uses carbon dioxide from the air as a raw material.

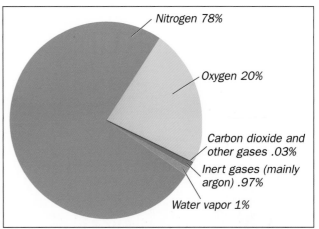

Nitrogen 78%

Oxygen 20%

Carbon dioxide and other gases .03%

Inert gases (mainly argon) .97%

Water vapor 1%

Air is composed of several different gases. This chart provides a simplified summary of the composition of air.

others are the result of pollution. In fact, air has a chemistry all its own. You will have the opportunity to investigate some aspects of the chemistry of air later in the module. ☐

QUESTIONS

Use library or Internet resources to answer one of the following questions:

1. Where did Earth's atmosphere come from?
2. Has the atmosphere always had the same composition?
3. Is the composition of the atmosphere changing? If so, what are the causes of this change? Write your answer as a paragraph with four to seven sentences.

5

Temperature and Density

This thermometer contains liquid. How does it work?

INTRODUCTION

Have you ever looked at a thermometer and wondered how it works? You may be surprised to learn that the thermometer was not invented until about 400 years ago. How did people measure temperature before that? Did they guess the temperature? Did they say something feels hot or cold? Thermometers are actually very easy to make from simple materials. In this lesson, you will build your own thermometer and learn something about how and why it works.

OBJECTIVES FOR THIS LESSON

Use a thermometer and discuss the purpose of its different parts.

Build a working thermometer and use it to measure temperature.

Discuss how your thermometer works and relate this to changes in the volume and density of matter.

Getting Started

1. Collect the plastic box of apparatus for your group and check the items against the materials list. Each plastic box contains a set of apparatus for each pair within your group.

MATERIALS FOR LESSON 5

For you

1 copy of Student Sheet 5.1: Building a Thermometer

1 copy of Student Sheet 5.2: Replacing the Liquid With Air

1 copy of Student Sheet 5.3: Heating the Metal Strip

1 copy of Student Sheet 5: Engineering for Expansion

For you and your lab partner

1 thermometer

1 piece of plastic tubing mounted in a stopper

1 rubber stopper with single hole

1 20 × 150-mm test tube

1 250-mL beaker containing 100 mL of colored water

1 black permanent marker

1 metric ruler

Access to hot and cold water baths

2. With your lab partner, closely examine the thermometer you have been given. Discuss with your partner the purpose of the different parts of the thermometer. The following questions will help you in your discussion:

A. Where is most of the liquid in your thermometer?

B. What is the temperature range of your thermometer (and what units does it measure in)?

C. What do you notice about the distances between the marks on the scale?

3. Hold the bulb of the thermometer (the red end) in your hand. Discuss the following questions with your partner:

A. What happens to the red liquid?

B. What temperature does it reach?

C. What happens to the reading when you let go of the bulb and hold on to the other end of the thermometer?

D. Why do you think the liquid in the thermometer moves?

4. Be prepared to discuss your observations and ideas with the rest of the class.

Inquiry 5.1
Building a Thermometer

PROCEDURE

1. Divide the contents of the plastic box between the two pairs in your group. How could you use the materials to build a thermometer? You have 5 minutes to discuss possible designs with your partner and draw your design on Student Sheet 5.1. Do *not* build the thermometer yet.

2. Your teacher will conduct a short brainstorming session and a discussion on thermometer design.

3. Follow the design discussed to build your thermometer.

4. Add a scale to the thermometer. This process is called calibration. To calibrate your thermometer, follow these instructions:

A. Place the test tube end of the thermometer in the cold water bath. Let it stand for about 5 minutes.

B. Without removing the test tube from the cold water bath, use the black permanent marker to make a mark on the plastic tubing at the water level.

C. Use the thermometer in the water bath to record the temperature of the water bath on Student Sheet 5.1.

D. Place the test tube in the hot water bath. Let it stand for about 5 minutes.

E. Mark the tubing and record the temperature as before.

F. Calculate the temperature difference between the two readings you made. Write your answer on the student sheet.

G. What is the distance in millimeters (mm) between the two marks on the plastic tubing? Write your measurement under Step 3 on Student Sheet 5.1.

H. Calculate the distance on your thermometer that is equal to 1 °C.

I. Use this information to figure out where 0 °C and 100 °C will be on your thermometer.

J. Mark off the temperature scale between 0 °C and 100 °C in 5 °C intervals. Label these intervals every 10 °C.

5. Once you have built and calibrated your thermometer, test it by measuring room temperature. Allow time for your thermometer to reach room temperature. What reading did your thermometer give for room temperature? Write your answer on the student sheet.

6. Measure room temperature with the laboratory thermometer. What reading did the laboratory thermometer give? Write your answer on the student sheet.

7. Answer the following questions on your student sheet: How accurate is your thermometer compared with the laboratory thermometer? How quickly does your thermometer respond to temperature changes? Is it quicker, slower, or the same as the laboratory thermometer?

When the temperature increases, what happens to the volume of water in your thermometer? When the temperature increases, do you think the mass of water in your thermometer changes? If you decreased the size of the thermometer bulb, how would the accuracy and the response time of your thermometer be affected? How could you improve the design of your thermometer to make it more accurate?

Inquiry 5.2
Replacing the Liquid With Air

PROCEDURE

1. Redesign your thermometer so that it uses air. Here are some problems to think about:

A. How will you stop the air from escaping?

B. How will you measure the distance the air moves up the column?

2. Draw your design on Student Sheet 5.2. After a short class discussion, build your thermometer and try to calibrate it.

3. Answer the following questions on the student sheet. What problems did you encounter when calibrating your air-filled thermometer? How did the response of your air-filled thermometer compare with that of your liquid-filled one?

Inquiry 5.3
Heating the Metal Strip

PROCEDURE

1. Your teacher will pass around a metal strip. What do you notice about both sides of the strip?

2. What do you think will happen to the metal strip when it is heated? Write your answer on Student Sheet 5.3.

3. Observe what happens to the strip as your teacher heats it. Answer the following question on the student sheet: What did you observe when the strip was heated?

4. Observe the strip after it cools. Answer the following question on the student sheet: What happens to the strip after it cools?

5. Observe what happens to the strip when your teacher heats the other side of it. Answer the following questions on the student sheet: What did you observe when the strip was heated on the other side? Why do you think the strip behaves this way?

REFLECTING ON WHAT YOU'VE DONE

1. Answer the following questions in your science notebook:

   A. *What do these three inquiries tell you about how the volume of matter is affected by temperature?*

   B. *How does the change in the volume of the air differ from the change in the volume of the liquid?*

   C. *How does this change in volume affect the density of solids, liquids, and gases?*

   D. *When measuring the density of a substance, why is it important to record the temperature of the substance?*

   E. *Are there any other uses for the expansion and contraction of matter?*

   F. *Could expansion or contraction cause problems? (You may wish to look at the reader about the Trans-Alaska Pipeline on pages 52–55 to help you answer this question.)*

2. Read "Changing Temperature, Changing Density", on page 43.

CHANGING TEMPERATURE, CHANGING DENSITY

Most matter increases in volume when it gets hotter. For example, if an iron rod is heated, it will get longer and fatter and its density will decrease. This happens because the mass of the rod stays the same, but its volume increases. The increase in the volume of matter with increasing temperature is called expansion. When cooled down, most matter decreases in volume and increases in density. This decrease in volume is called contraction.

A few substances behave differently when heated or cooled. Water is one such substance. When water approaches freezing, it expands and becomes less dense, which is why water pipes sometimes burst when they freeze and why icebergs float.

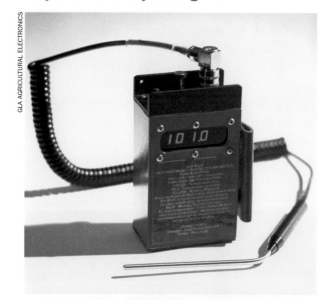

This horse thermometer has a digital readout. Veterinarians can use it in conjunction with a computer. It does not use changing density to measure temperature. Do you know how it works?

Some thermometers use bimetal strips to measure temperature. In this lesson, you may get some ideas about how these thermometers work.

MEASURING TEMPERATURE BY DEGREES

"How cold is it outside?" "Is your soup hot enough?" How many times have you been asked questions about temperature? Usually, we answer them according to how things feel to us. We compare temperatures to our own body temperature. People have always compared temperatures in this way. However, sometimes you need to know *exactly* how hot or cold something is. For example, if you cook a pizza in an oven that is too hot, it may burn—so you need to know the temperature of the oven.

About 400 years ago, some scientists began to tackle the problem of measuring temperature. Galileo was one of the first.

He made a thermoscope. This was a device that could be used to compare temperatures. Look at the picture of the thermoscope. Can you figure out how it worked?

It took another scientist, Olas Roemer, a Dane who was interested in astronomy and meteorology, to come up with a way of comparing temperatures measured with different devices. In 1701, Roemer calibrated his temperature-measuring devices according to the temperatures of ice water and the human body. He had made the first thermometer.

A thermoscope built to one of Galileo's designs. Thermoscopes were used to compare temperatures but had no standardized scale.

COURTESY OF THE LIBRARY OF CONGRESS

Galileo built some of the earliest thermoscopes, which are thermometers without scales.

Roemer invented the first
useful temperature scale.

In 1742, Anders Celsius
invented the Celsius (or
centigrade) scale.

William Thomson started his
temperature scale with the
lowest possible temperature.

Another scientist, this time from Holland, borrowed Roemer's ideas. His name was G. Daniel Fahrenheit. Fahrenheit altered Roemer's scale. He used the melting point of a salt-and-water slush as his zero point and the human body temperature as his high point. He divided the space between the two points into 96 degrees. The scale was later adjusted so that its calibration points were at 32 °F for ice melting and 212 °F for water boiling. On the adjusted scale, human body temperature became 98.6 °F. The new scale was named after Fahrenheit and is still used today.

About 30 years later, in 1742, another scientist, Anders Celsius from Sweden, came up with a new scale. Celsius designated the melting point of ice as 100 °C and the boiling point of water (at sea level) as 0 °C. After Celsius's death, the scale was reversed so that the melting point of ice became 0 °C and the boiling point of water (at sea level) became 100 °C. This scale, called the Celsius (or centigrade) scale, was popular because it used two temperatures that most people easily understand. It's now used all around the world. This scale has

one big problem. All temperatures below zero become negative numbers. Can you really have a negative temperature? Wouldn't it be better to start a scale at the lowest possible temperature and work your way up?

About 100 years later, in 1848, British physicist William Thomson could see the advantage of just such a scale. By that time, work done by Thomson and other scientists on how energy behaves in the universe led him to develop a scale that placed the absolute lowest possible temperature at zero. This temperature is the same as −273 °C and is called absolute zero. An object at absolute zero contains no heat energy. Thomson borrowed the divisions on Celsius's scale and made the melting point of ice 273 degrees. What happened to the Thomson scale? It is still used by scientists around the world, who consider it to be the most useful temperature scale.

Thomson was such a clever scientist and inventor that the British government made him a lord and gave him the title Lord Kelvin. So his scale became the Kelvin scale, and temperature is measured in kelvins (abbreviated as K). ☐

JUST A LOAD OF HOT AIR

© FERNE SALTZMAN/ALBUQUERQUE INTERNATIONAL BALLOON FIESTA

Hot air balloons can be made into many fun shapes. But why do they need to be so big?

Just a load of hot air! That's what you will find inside a hot air balloon. But why does hot air help a balloon rise? Hot air balloons rely on the fact that the density of air decreases as it gets hotter. A gas burner, mounted above a balloon's basket, is used to heat the air inside the balloon. As the air heats, it increases in volume, or expands. You already know that density is equal to mass divided by volume. So what happens if the volume of the air inside a balloon increases while the mass of the air stays the same? The density of the air in the balloon decreases. When the average density of the balloon (including the burner, basket, and passengers) becomes less than the density of the surrounding air, the balloon begins to rise. It floats in the air.

The balloonist can alter the height of the balloon by switching the burner on and off. If the burner is turned off, the air inside the balloon cools. As the air cools, its volume decreases, it becomes denser, and the balloon goes down. The balloonist can also let some of the hot air out of the top of the balloon to make the balloon go down. If the burner is turned on, the air in the balloon becomes hotter. The air takes up more volume, becomes less dense, and the balloon rises.

The first free flight of a hot air balloon was in 1783, when the Montgolfier brothers sent a sheep, a duck, and a rooster into the air in a balloon made from linen. A few weeks later, in the first manned free flight, two Frenchmen, using burning straw as a heat source, piloted a Montgolfier balloon

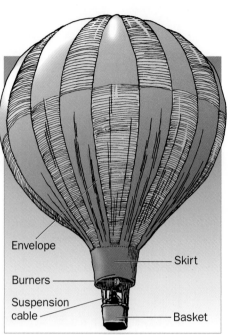

The hot air balloon rises because its average density is less than the surrounding air.

Envelope

Skirt

Burners

Suspension cable

Basket

COURTESY OF SAN DIEGO AEROSPACE MUSEUM

This is a scale model of the balloon used for the first manned balloon flight. The balloon reached a height of almost 1000 meters and stayed aloft for 25 minutes.

about 5 miles across Paris.

Today, most hot air balloons are made from ripstop nylon and use propane gas burners instead of straw. The average hot air balloon is as tall as a seven-story building, is about 20 meters across at the widest part, and is big enough to carry four adults. Hot air balloons can be built in many shapes. □

QUESTION

How does a balloon pilot use density to control the altitude of a balloon?

Density Creates Currents

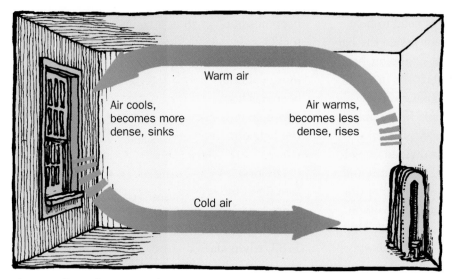

A convection cell can occur in a room.

How do changes in density move matter? This movement involves a process called convection. To understand how convection works, imagine a room in a house, like the one shown in the picture above.

One side of the room has a heater; on the opposite wall is a window. On a cold winter day, when the heat is on, air near the heater will warm up. What happens to hot air? It expands, becomes less dense, and rises. On reaching the ceiling, it is pushed along by more hot air rising behind it. The heated air starts to cool down the farther it drifts from the heater, and this process is speeded up when it meets the cold window. As the air cools, it becomes more dense, sinks to the floor, and eventually completes a circuit of the room. A circular convection current is set up. Circular currents like this are called convection cells.

Convection currents like this also take place in the atmosphere (see the picture below).

We encounter these convection currents as wind. Where do you think the heat energy for these convection currents comes from? Real winds are more complex than what is shown in the picture, but all winds are created by changes in density brought about by temperature differences. How do you think the winds shown in the picture would be different at night?

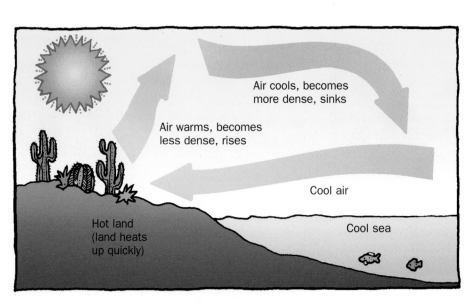

A convection cell can also occur in the atmosphere.

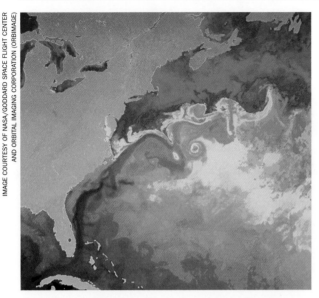

The Gulf Stream is an ocean current that is driven, in part, by convection. It carries warm water from the tropics toward the North Pole.

Convection works in liquids as well as in gases. Ocean currents have several different causes, many of which are due to changes in density. Some ocean currents are convection currents (see the picture on the left).

Under the tropical sun, water at the equator warms up. At the cold poles, seawater cools down and sinks. Convection cells are set up with warm water moving along the surface to the poles and deep cold water flowing toward the equator. Changes in density, caused by changes in salinity (the amount of salt in the water), are also important in the formation of ocean currents. Ice formation near the poles leaves salt behind in the remaining water. This denser, more saline water sinks, creating its own density-driven currents. Surface winds also set surface currents into motion.

Moving and Making Mountains

Convection currents can move or split whole continents. Radioactive substances deep within the Earth provide the heat that drives these currents (see the picture below illustrating how these convection cells work).

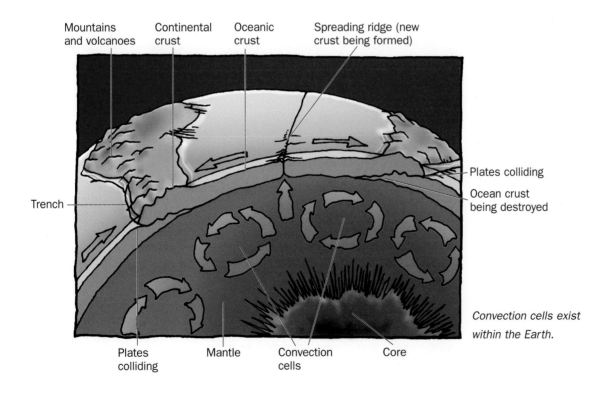

Convection cells exist within the Earth.

Earth's surface is made up of a series of giant plates that fit together like a moving spherical jigsaw. These plates can be made from two types of crustal material: dense oceanic crust and comparatively less dense continental crust. The hot rocks deep in the mantle behave like a soft plastic. These warm, less dense rocks move up, pushing aside rock that lies on the surface. These convection currents create some of the mountain ridges found on the ocean bed. The Mid-Atlantic Ridge is one example. Sometimes these ridges emerge at the surface of the ocean as islands.

Convection currents in the Earth produce volcanoes, like this one near Iceland in the North Atlantic.

Eventually this volcano formed an island called Surtsey.

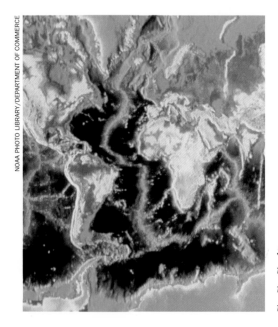

Surtsey is part of a mountain system, formed as a result of convection currents, that extends under the Atlantic Ocean.

Great ranges of fold mountains are formed where plates collide. Mount Everest, the highest mountain in the world, is in the Himalayas of Nepal. These mountains are being formed as the plate carrying India collides with the plate carrying Asia.

As plates expand, they push against other plates. When plates that consist of two pieces of continent push against one another, they may buckle up along their boundaries to form great fold mountains (see the photo of Mount Everest). They may also slide past one another, as at the famous San Andreas fault in California.

Earthquakes can occur as the plates slide past one another or build mountains. If a plate of more dense oceanic crust pushes against less dense continental crust, what do you think happens? The more dense ocean crust sinks down to create ocean trenches. Evidence for this process is provided in the form of the volcanoes and earthquakes that are caused by all this activity.

Why is density important? Changes in density drive many of Earth's processes. Next time you climb a mountain or hear about an earthquake or a tornado, think about how density and density changes have an impact on human lives! ☐

QUESTION
Big birds such as vultures and hawks can often be seen gliding around and around over big parking lots on sunny days, without even flapping their wings. Why?

The Trans-Alaska Pipeline: Meeting Nature's Challenges

Trans-Alaska Pipeline: Facts and Figures

- The pipeline is 1287 kilometers long. Each piece is 127 centimeters in diameter.
- The pipeline crosses 34 major rivers and streams and 3 mountain ranges.
- Construction was started in 1973 and completed in 1977. The cost was $8 billion.

The Trans-Alaska Pipeline (in red) stretches from Valdez to Deadhorse.

It was 1968, and the United States was concerned about its oil supply. With war brewing in the Middle East and an oil embargo threatening, where would the United States get the petroleum it needed? How could the country become less dependent on oil imports in the years ahead?

Just when concerns were getting serious, geologists discovered the largest oil field in this country—in Prudhoe Bay on the northern slope of Alaska. Part of the problem was solved.

But during the winter, the waters of Prudhoe Bay are frozen solid. For much of the year, they cannot be reached by sea-going oil tankers. How could those billions of gallons of oil be transported to the lower United States? The answer: Build a pipeline!

The people who took on this problem

PHOTO COURTESY ALYESKA PIPELINE SERVICE COMPANY

Fiberglass insulation is being wrapped around the pipeline to reduce heat loss.

would find themselves involved in one of the most difficult engineering challenges of this century. To solve it, they had to focus on three features of the Alaskan territory: permafrost, earthquakes, and temperature extremes.

Watching Out for Permafrost

At first, the engineers assumed that the pipeline would be buried underground. That's how most pipelines are built, after all.

But no one had ever built a pipeline in a place like Alaska, where it gets so cold that in many parts of the state, the subsoil is permanently frozen. This deep soil, which never thaws, is called permafrost.

Planners realized that the pipeline couldn't be buried in the permafrost, because the heat of the oil could cause the icy soil to melt. If the icy soil melted, the pipe would sag and it might leak. In winter, the soil around the pipe would freeze again. This freeze-thaw cycle could cause the pipe to move enough to cause serious damage.

To avoid these complications, the engineers made an important decision: About one-half of the pipeline (about 700 kilometers) would have to be built above ground. They supported the pipe with refrigeration posts that are topped with aluminum radiators. The posts conduct heat away from the soil. The pipeline is also wrapped in 10 centimeters of fiberglass insulation. Both of these measures help to keep the permafrost solid.

Blowing Hot and Cold

A second challenge was Alaska's temperature, which ranges between −60 °C and 35 °C. Because the metals from which the pipeline is made expand and contract with changes in temperature, the pipeline had to be built to accommodate changes in length. The engineers estimated that

© KEN M. JOHNS/PHOTO RESEARCHERS, INC.

The pipeline was mounted on posts above the frozen ground. The aluminum radiators on top of the posts conduct heat—lost from the pipeline—away from the soil. The zig-zag in the pipeline allows it to expand and contract without breaking.

a 304-meter segment of pipeline could shrink by as much as 0.3 meter in the coldest weather and expand by an equal amount during the warmest season. That doesn't sound like much of a change, unless you remember that the pipeline is nearly 1500 kilometers long! If the pipeline were straight, even a small change in each segment of the pipeline would be disastrous. The pipeline would either snap if it contracted too much or buckle if it expanded.

To prevent the pipeline from breaking, the designers used a zig-zag configuration. These bends help relieve the effect of contraction and expansion.

Accounting for Earthquakes
As if these extreme temperatures weren't enough,

engineers had to deal with another big problem: earthquakes. Earthquakes are fairly common in Alaska. In fact, the largest earthquake ever to occur in the United States (measuring 9.2 on the Richter scale) took place in southern Alaska. The engineers had to build a pipeline that could survive such an event intact.

They designed a two-part system of "shoes" and "anchors" that hold the pipeline in place at weak areas (faults) where earthquakes have occurred, yet allow it to move enough so that it does not fall off its supports if the ground moves. At the Denali fault zone, where earthquake activity has been heavy, the pipeline is designed to move up to 6 meters side to side and 1.5 meters up and down. ❑

QUESTIONS
1. How did engineers overcome the challenge of a 95 °C temperature range when designing the Trans-Alaska Pipeline?
2. What is the difference between conduction and radiation? Use a dictionary or other references to help you answer this question.

6

Applying the Heat

Even Cordon Bleu chefs use heat to change matter.

INTRODUCTION

Have you ever baked a chocolate cake? After mixing the ingredients, you have a sticky brown liquid. You put it in the oven at a certain temperature. Twenty minutes later . . . presto! You have a chocolate sponge. Now for the chocolate topping. You slowly heat the chocolate until it melts. Then you spread it quickly on top of the cake before it turns solid again. The next stage? Well, eat it, of course!

It's time to stop thinking about food and get on with the science. Of course, what you just read contains a great deal of science. Most of the ingredients in a cake change when they are heated (see Figure 6.1). But each one changes in a different way. The way they behave depends on their characteristic properties.

The changes that occur in a cake mixture when it is heated are very complex. Some of the substances in the mixture change phase; others break down or combine with one another to form new substances. It is easier to examine the effect of heating on other, simpler substances. In this lesson, you will discuss how heating affects some familiar substances. Next, you will investigate six different substances as they are heated. You will be asked to make careful observations, accurately record them, and discuss your results.

OBJECTIVES FOR THIS LESSON

Review what you already know about how heating affects substances.

Observe and record the effects of heating on different substances.

Discuss the results of the inquiry.

Figure 6.1 *What effect does heat have on the ingredients of a cake?*

MATERIALS FOR LESSON 6

For you

1 copy of Student Sheet 6.1: Applying the Heat

1 copy of Student Sheet 6: Review for Characteristic Properties

1 pair of safety goggles

For your group

1 burner

1 250-mL beaker

1 test tube clamp

5 test tubes

1 lab scoop

1 test tube brush

1 test tube containing sulfur

5 jars containing:
   Ammonium chloride
   Copper (II) carbonate
   Copper (II) sulfate
   Sodium chloride
   Zinc oxide

Getting Started

1. Take 5 minutes to think of two familiar household substances that you have heated. In your science notebook, write what happened when you heated the two substances.

2. Your teacher will lead a brainstorming session on heating substances. Be ready to contribute your examples and ideas to the discussion.

Inquiry 6.1
Heating Substances

PROCEDURE

1. Your teacher will explain the purpose of Inquiry 6.1 and review safety procedures.

2. Your teacher will demonstrate the procedure you will follow for heating substances. Watch the demonstration carefully.

3. Copy the information from the class table onto Table 1 on Student Sheet 6.1.

4. Participate in a class discussion.

5. You will be working in groups of four. One member of your group should collect the plastic box containing the apparatus. Check the contents of the plastic box against the materials list.

6. Read Steps 7 through 17 below *before* starting to heat the substances.

7. Your teacher will allocate a workstation to your group. Each workstation has a burner. Check that it is ready for use before asking your teacher to ignite it. Make sure you carefully follow the procedure demonstrated by your teacher for using your burner.

8. Place one lab scoop of the first substance into a test tube.

9. Write the name of the first substance you are going to heat in the first column of Table 1 on Student Sheet 6.1.

10. Examine the substance carefully. In the second column of Table 1, record its appearance before you start heating it.

Figure 6.2 *Hold the test tube over the flame and keep it moving to heat the substance evenly. (The burner shown here is an alcohol burner, yours may differ from this one.)*

11. Attach the test tube clamp near the mouth of the test tube.

12. Heat the bottom of the test tube containing the substance for 1–2 minutes. Keep the tube moving to heat the substance evenly (see Figure 6.2).

13. Observe any changes and record your observations in the third column of Table 1.

SAFETY TIP

Do not walk around while holding the hot test tube.

SAFETY TIP

Hold the test tube at an angle of about 45° to the flame. Make sure you are not pointing the open end of the test tube at yourself or anyone else.

14. Allow the test tube and the substance to cool for 1 minute. Place the test tube in the 250-mL beaker. In the fourth column of Table 1, record the appearance of the solid after it has cooled.

15. Use the same procedure to heat the other four substances in the jars.

16. Use the same procedure to observe, describe, and heat the sulfur. After cooling, return the test tube containing the sulfur to the plastic box. These test tubes may be used later by another class.

17. When you finish heating all six substances, extinguish the burner.

18. Make sure all the tubes are cool before disposing of the chemicals in the container provided for that purpose. *Do not* empty or clean the test tube containing the sulfur.

19. Use the test tube brush and water to clean the other test tubes thoroughly. Allow the tubes to drain and then stand them upside down in the 250-mL beaker. Return your apparatus to the plastic box.

20. Answer these questions on Student Sheet 6.1 and be prepared to discuss your answers with the rest of the class: Which substances (if any) showed no change when heated? Which of the substances produced new substances when they were heated? How can heating a substance help you to identify it?

REFLECTING ON WHAT YOU'VE DONE

1. Your teacher will conduct a class discussion. Be prepared to participate.

2. Read "Heat and Changing Matter."

HEAT AND CHANGING MATTER

You have discovered that heat affects different substances in different ways. When you heated one of the solids, it melted. Then when the substance cooled, it solidified again. Another substance turned into a gas and then turned back to a solid farther up the tube. When a substance changes from one phase to another it is called a phase change. Did any of the substances you heated exist in all three phases of matter (solid, liquid, and gas) within the test tube?

Many of the other substances changed their appearance when you heated them and did not return to their original form when they cooled. This is usually a sign that a chemical reaction has taken place. In a chemical reaction, one or more substances (called reactants) are changed into new substances (called products).

In Inquiry 6.1, the substances that underwent chemical reactions decomposed when they were heated and then formed products that did not look like the original substances. This type of chemical reaction is called thermal decomposition. Some of the substances you heated decomposed and gave off invisible gas as one of the products. Can you identify one of the substances that you heated that did this? What evidence do you have that an invisible gas may have been produced? There are many other types of chemical reactions. You will investigate some later in the module.

Some substances change in other ways when they are heated. Can you identify any of these changes? How could these types of changes be useful to people? The way a substance behaves when it is heated is a characteristic property of that substance.

The Properties of Asbestos: The Pros and Cons

Many substances burn when they are heated. Others melt or evaporate. Some substances, such as asbestos, do not change when they are heated. This property can be very useful. For centuries, people have known that this fibrous mineral has many useful properties. It is fire resistant. It does not melt or react with air, at least not until it gets very hot. One form of the mineral withstands temperatures up to 2750 °C. It is a very good insulator. It is strong. It resists acid. It is chemically inactive. It can be woven into cloth. Asbestos has some very useful properties, and it is readily available at a low cost.

This is a close-up of a piece of asbestos rock. Can you see the fibers?

Asbestos is a naturally occurring mineral that is mined.

The Romans used asbestos for lamp wicks. Egyptians used it to make burial cloths. In modern times, asbestos has been used in roofing and flooring, electrical and heat insulation, and brake linings. Because of its fire-resistant properties, asbestos has been used for a wide variety of other purposes, from theater curtains to firefighters' suits and gloves.

Until the 1970s, asbestos was widely used and asbestos mining and production were important

These firefighters are wearing suits woven from asbestos to protect them from the intense heat produced by a fire in an oil refinery.

industrial activities in the United States. Today, asbestos mining is banned in this country, and the use of asbestos has been strictly regulated.

Why? It is now known that inhaling asbestos fibers can cause lung disease. Asbestos releases tiny particles that remain suspended in the air. Once inhaled, these downy particles can remain in the lungs for decades. They cause delicate lung tissue to stiffen. A lung disease, called asbestosis, and a type of cancer may occur years after the original exposure.

Today, construction companies are not allowed to use asbestos as insulation or fireproofing in new buildings. Workers who are exposed to asbestos must wear protective clothing. They have to shower and change clothes before going home.

Government regulations also apply to some buildings that had already been built when the new laws were passed. For example, schools that contain asbestos products have had to remove them.

So, there's good news and bad news. Regulating the mining, manufacture, and use of

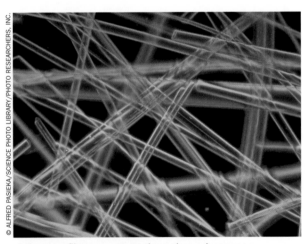

Asbestos fibers as seen through a microscope

asbestos has reduced the health risk that millions of Americans were being exposed to daily. But nothing has yet been found that can replace asbestos. However, researchers are exploring the use of synthetic fibers, fiberglass, and plastics as asbestos substitutes.

It's a trade-off: using a substance that has many useful properties versus having a safer environment. In the United States, the decision has been made. What other similar trade-offs can you think of? ☐

Asbestos has been removed from some buildings to reduce the risk of inhabitants being exposed. How do the workers removing the asbestos minimize the risks to themselves?

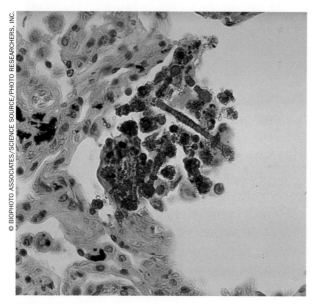

Asbestos fibers in the human lung can cause several diseases, some fatal.

QUESTION

Many substances with useful properties have some undesirable ones as well. Use library and Internet resources to answer the following question: What are some properties and some of the pros and cons of using one of the following substances: mercury, plutonium, or benzene?

Just a Phase

How are heat and phase change involved
in powering this old locomotive?

COURTESY OF THE LIBRARY OF CONGRESS/PHOTOASSIST, INC.

INTRODUCTION

Do you eat spaghetti? To cook spaghetti, you fill
a large pot with water, perhaps add some salt,
put the pot on the stove, and turn on the heat.
When the water boils, you add the spaghetti, stir
it well, and simmer for about 8 minutes. Why do
you need to cook it for 8 minutes? What happens if you are in a hurry and want to cook it
faster? Look at Figure 7.1 on page 65. Will
"turning up the heat" raise the temperature and
make the spaghetti cook faster? Does the boiling
water get hotter the longer it boils? Why don't
the cooking instructions tell you to cook the
spaghetti as quickly as you can?

You may be surprised to learn that a lot of
interesting science takes place when you heat
water. In this lesson, you will look at and think
about what happens when solid water, or ice, is
heated until it boils and beyond.

OBJECTIVES FOR THIS LESSON

Discuss your current knowledge of
phase change.

Observe what happens to ice as it is
heated.

Measure the temperature of ice water
as it is heated.

Plot a graph of your measurements.

Interpret your graph and other
observations.

Figure 7.1 *Can you make simmering spaghetti cook faster by turning up the heat?*

MATERIALS FOR LESSON 7

For you
1 copy of Student Sheet 7.1: Heating Ice Water

For your group
1 burner
1 burner stand
1 thermometer
1 250-mL beaker
    3–4 ice cubes (or crushed ice)
    Access to a clock or watch with a second hand

Getting Started

1. After reading the Introduction, discuss the following questions with other members of your group:

A. How could you make spaghetti cook faster?

B. Why does ice melt?

C. Why can you play in the snow when it is warm outside?

D. Why doesn't ice melt immediately when you add it to a soft drink?

E. Are things that are boiling always hot? Are things that are frozen always cold?

F. What are some of your own questions about what happens when ice melts and water boils?

2. Record your group's and your own ideas in your science notebook. You will be asked to present some of these ideas during a short brainstorming session.

BOILING OIL

This old Texas gusher shows crude oil, under pressure from surrounding gas, being forced up from under the ground. Once out of the ground, the oil must be processed.

The next time you visit a gas station, look at some of the products sold there. In addition to gasoline, you'll probably find diesel fuel, kerosene, engine oil, gear grease, and other lubricants. All of these substances help keep cars and other vehicles running. Where do they come from?

A car's ability to cruise down the highway—and possibly even the highway itself—is based on the activity of a variety of organisms that lived in the sea hundreds of millions of years ago. These organisms died, but they only partially decomposed. Over millions of years, their remains became compressed, were heated, and eventually turned into crude oil and natural gas. By drilling down into the rocks where the crude oil and gas are found, it is possible to extract it.

Crude oil is very thick, comes in a variety of unusual colors (including red), and smells pretty awful. How is crude oil made into substances that can be used in cars? When crude oil is boiled, a lot of interesting things happen. You see, crude oil is not a single substance. It's a mixture.

As crude oil is heated, some of the substances in it start to boil. Substances with low boiling points, like gasoline, are the first to boil. Kerosene is next, followed by fuel oils (some of which are used to make diesel fuel) and then

All of these different oils (or fractions) were obtained from crude oil by the process of fractional distillation. Each fraction has a different boiling point.

Crude oil is separated into its different components in fractionating and cracking towers like these in Saudi Arabia.

Oil is a very valuable resource, and people go to great lengths to extract it.

heavier oils (which are often used for lubrication). In the end, only the substances with high boiling points (more than 370 °C) are left—as a dark, gooey, smelly mess. But even these materials have a use. They make up asphalt, which is used as a surface for the highways on which cars travel!

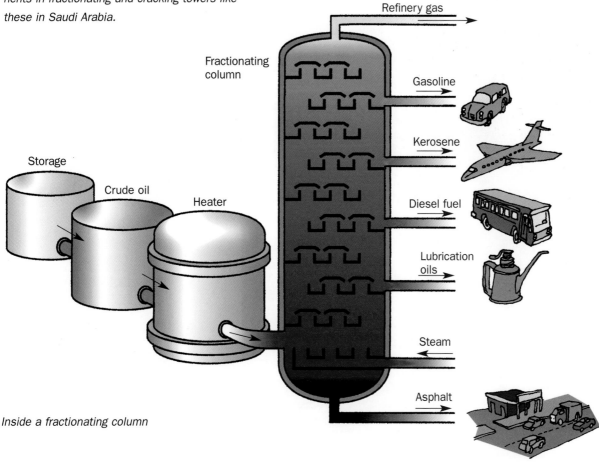

Refinery gas

Gasoline

Kerosene

Diesel fuel

Lubrication oils

Steam

Asphalt

Fractionating column

Storage

Crude oil

Heater

Inside a fractionating column

All this boiling takes place at an oil refinery. The crude oil is heated in special towers called fractionating towers or columns. In different levels of the towers, gases produced when the crude oil is heated are condensed. The substances that come from crude oil are not only used to make fuels and lubricants. They are also used as raw materials for hundreds of industrial processes—from making glues to plastic bottles and even clothing. □

QUESTION

Examine this picture. How many of the items in it, including car parts, could be made from oil?

How many objects in this picture could be made from oil?

LOST WAX CASTING:
Exploiting Melting Points for Art and Industry

Knowledge of melting points is very important for people who work with metal. Let's look at the goldsmiths who live in a small village in Côte d'Ivoire (Ivory Coast), West Africa, as an example. They make jewelry and other items by using a technique that has been in existence for thousands of years. It is called "lost wax casting."

In this technique, an artist produces a clay mold around an easily carved substance: wax. When the mold is heated,

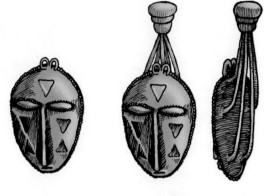

The artist carves a model in wax (usually beeswax). Wax is soft, and the artist can use it to produce intricate carvings. After completing the model, he attaches tiny wax rods (called sprues) to it that will produce channels in the mold for draining the wax and receiving the gold.

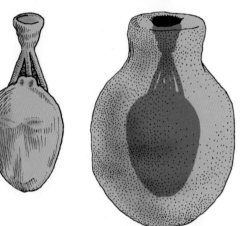

The artist covers the wax figure with several layers of fine wet clay. Coarse clay is then added in layers to complete the mold. The clay mold is placed in an oven and heated until it hardens. The wax melts and runs out of the mold (in other words, it's lost!).

The wax model is carefully cleaned before the first layer of fine clay is added.

the wax, which has a melting point less than 70 °C, melts away. The hard clay mold can then be used to produce jewelry made from metals with high melting points. The artists often use gold, which has a melting point of more than 1000 °C.

The pictures here show the major steps in lost wax casting. In these pictures the artist is using gold. □

NATIONAL MUSEUM OF AFRICAN ART, H 2 EBR 13

Air is pumped by hand bellows into a charcoal furnace. This produces the high temperature needed to melt gold.

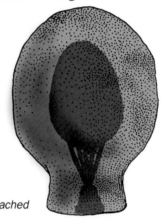

Pieces of gold are placed in a crucible.

The crucible is attached to the mold. The two parts are then sealed together using more clay.

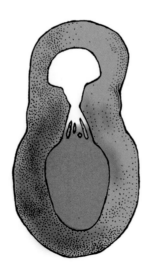

The mold and gold are heated together in the furnace. When the gold has melted, the mold is turned over so that the metal flows into it. The mold cools. The clay mold is cracked off, leaving a casting.

The artist files away a few rough edges, and the jewelry is ready.

NATIONAL MUSEUM OF AFRICAN ART, 85-19-12

The lost wax method has been used to produce a wide variety of objects, including this figure of a king from Nigeria.

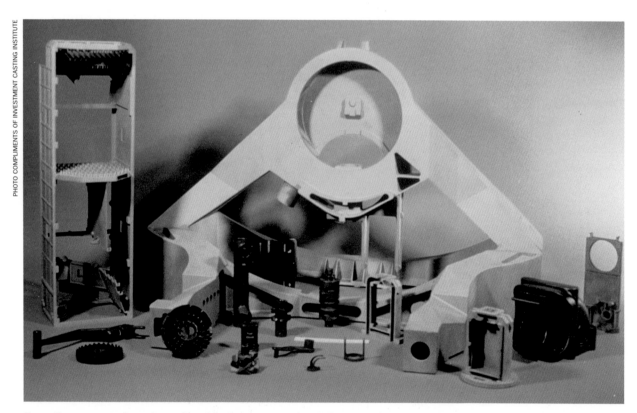

PHOTO COMPLIMENTS OF INVESTMENT CASTING INSTITUTE

Recently, new uses have been found for lost wax casting. It is one technique used to produce precision parts, such as these—designed using computers—for aircraft and other machines.

Changing Matter and Mass

A glacier in Alaska calves a new iceberg. The iceberg weighs thousands of tons. What happens to the mass of its matter when it melts?

INTRODUCTION

In Glacier Bay, Alaska, 12 giant glaciers meet the sea. As the seawater undermines and melts these huge rivers of ice, icebergs break off, or "calve." Chunks of ice, some more than 60 meters (200 feet) high and weighing thousands of tons, plunge with a huge splash into the sea. Because ice is less dense than water, the icebergs float. For a few weeks in the summer, they may provide floating islands for the local wildlife before becoming part of the sea themselves. What happens to the mass of a 50,000-ton iceberg when it melts? For that matter, what happens to the mass of a melting ice cube in a cup of soda, the mass of water as it freezes in the refrigerator, or the mass of boiling water in a kettle when it turns into steam?

What happens to the mass of matter when it changes phase? In this lesson, you will discuss and try to answer this question.

OBJECTIVES FOR THIS LESSON

Discuss what happens to the mass of substances when they change state.

Conduct an experiment to investigate whether any changes of mass occur when ice melts.

Discuss sources of experimental error within your experiment.

Design an inquiry to test your own prediction about any changes of mass that may occur when water freezes.

At this hot spring in Yellowstone Park, what happens to the mass of water when it evaporates? Does the water vapor have the same mass as the liquid water that formed it?

MATERIALS FOR LESSON 8

For you

1 copy of Student Sheet 8.1: Investigating Mass and Melting

1 copy of Student Sheet 8.2: Investigating Mass and Freezing

For you and your lab partner

1 plastic soda bottle with screw cap

1 250-mL beaker

1 paper towel

2 ice cubes, crushed
   Access to an electronic balance

Getting Started

1. What happens to the mass of matter when it changes phase? Write in your science notebook your prediction of what will happen to the mass of the matter in the following situations:

- the mass of an ice cube when it melts
- the mass of the water in an ice cube tray when it freezes
- the mass of the water in a tea kettle when it boils

2. Your teacher will record your predictions. Be prepared to contribute your predictions for each phase change.

Inquiry 8.1
Investigating Mass and Melting

PROCEDURE

1. One member of your group should collect the plastic box containing the apparatus. Divide the apparatus equally between each pair in your group.

2. In this inquiry, you will work with your partner to test your prediction about what will happen to the mass of ice when it melts. Examine your apparatus carefully. Discuss with your partner how you could use this apparatus, crushed ice, and an electronic balance to test your prediction.

3. Under Step 1 on Student Sheet 8.1, write the procedure you will use to investigate what happens to the mass of ice when it melts.

4. Your teacher will ask some pairs of students to share their procedures with the whole class. Be prepared to contribute your ideas to the discussion.

5. During the discussion, the class will agree on a procedure for the experiment. Write the class procedure under Step 2 on the student sheet.

6. Design a result table under Step 3 on the student sheet.

7. Begin the procedure. Record all of your results in your results table.

8. While the ice is melting, complete Steps 1 and 2 in Inquiry 8.2.

9. When the ice melts, measure the mass of the bottle and water (as outlined in the class procedure) and record the mass of the apparatus in your results table. Don't forget to wipe any condensation off the *outside* of the beaker with a dry paper towel.

10. Answer the following questions in Steps 4a and 4b on Student Sheet 8.1: What happened to the mass of the ice when it melted? Why did you use a sealed container for this experiment?

11. You will be asked to contribute your results to a class results table. Use the data from all the pairs to complete Table 1 on Student Sheet 8.1.

12. Did all of the pairs obtain the same result? Complete Step 6 on Student Sheet 8.1.

13. Participate in a class discussion on experimental error.

14. Compare the measurements you entered in Table 1. Use them to complete Steps 7a through 7d on the student sheet: Which measurements are very different from the others? Eliminate the very different measurements and use the remaining measurements to calculate the average change in mass. What was the most frequent measurement obtained for change of mass? What do you conclude from these results?

Inquiry 8.2
Investigating Mass and Freezing

PROCEDURE

1. Do you think any change in mass occurs when water freezes? Discuss your ideas with your partner.

2. How could you find out whether any change in mass occurs when water freezes? Design an experiment to answer this question. Describe your ideas for a procedure under Step 1 on Student Sheet 8.2.

3. Your teacher will ask you to describe your procedure. After a discussion, one student in your class will do the experiment based on the class procedure. Under Step 2 on the student sheet, record the mass of the sealed bottle of water used in the experiment.

4. You will revisit this experiment in a later lesson. When you have the results of this experiment, complete Step 3 on Student Sheet 8.2.

REFLECTING ON WHAT YOU'VE DONE

1. Be prepared for a class discussion on the conservation of mass.

2. Write a paragraph in your science notebook explaining how conservation of mass applies to melting.

9

The Mystery Object

Careful laboratory work is an important part of science. In this lesson, you will test some of your lab skills.

INTRODUCTION

This lesson is the assessment for Part 1: Characteristic Properties of Matter. The assessment is in two sections. In Section A, you will work by yourself to investigate a mystery object. You will use your measurement skills, your knowledge of density, and a data table to determine the substance that makes up your mystery object. Section B consists of several multiple choice questions. Some of these will require you to use your knowledge and skills to interpret data tables, diagrams, graphs, and experiments. Your teacher will use the results of this assessment to evaluate how well you can apply the concepts, knowledge, and skills you learned in the first part of the module.

OBJECTIVES FOR THIS LESSON

Discover the identity of the matter that makes up your mystery object.

Use your knowledge and skills to solve problems related to the characteristic properties of matter.

Getting Started

1. Your teacher will assign you to one set of apparatus and tell you which balance to use.

2. Follow along as your teacher reviews the guidelines for the assessment:

A. Immediately check your apparatus against the materials list.

B. You will work individually and should not talk to other students.

C. Answer all of the questions.

D. Do the performance assessment (Inquiry 9.1) first.

E. As soon as you finish the performance assessment, begin the written assessment.

F. You have 15 minutes to do each section of the assessment and 5 minutes to check your answers.

G. Three or four minutes before the end of the lesson, hand in Student Sheet 9. Follow your teacher's instructions for cleaning up.

MATERIALS FOR LESSON 9

For you

- 1 copy of Student Sheet 9: Assessment
- 1 100-mL graduated cylinder
- 1 250-mL beaker
- 1 metric ruler
- 1 loupe (double-eye magnifier)
- 1 mystery object
  Access to water
  Access to an electronic balance

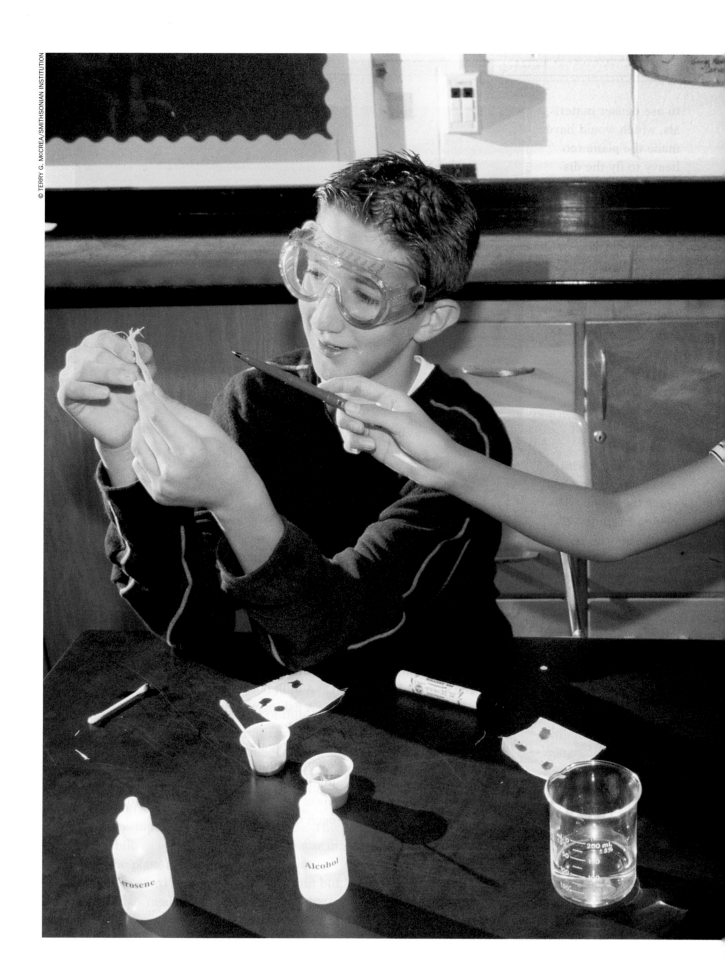

PART 2 Mixtures and Solutions

10

Starting the Anchor Activity

*What materials are chosen to make these sneakers?
How are these choices made?*

© HENRY HORESTEIN/STOCK, BOSTON/PNI

INTRODUCTION

In this lesson, you will begin the Anchor Activity, which you will work on over the next several weeks. What is an Anchor Activity? It is a project that gives you the opportunity to apply what you have learned in the module to the world around you. In this Anchor Activity, you and a partner will select a simple manufactured object. You will investigate the chemistry, technology, and history of the object by doing research at the library and on the Internet. You will then compile the information you have collected to create an exhibit. You will also give an oral presentation on one of the materials that makes up the object you choose. The work you do for this Anchor Activity will be an important part of your grade for this module.

OBJECTIVES FOR THIS LESSON

Select a simple manufactured object to research.

Conduct library and Internet research on the major materials that make up the object you have chosen.

Create an exhibit based on your research.

Give an oral presentation on one of the materials that makes up the object you have chosen.

Getting Started

1. Contribute to a class discussion on the reader from Lesson 9, "Choosing Materials for Pedal-Powered Flight," and the accompanying questions.

2. Read "The Right Material" on page 88.

3. Your teacher may have brought a bicycle to class. It is an example of a manufactured object. Discuss the choice of materials that make up the bicycle. After the class discussion, work with the rest of your group to complete Table 1 on Student Sheet 10a. List the function, the type of material, and the properties of the material for each bicycle part.

Introducing the Anchor Activity

PROCEDURE

1. After your teacher gives you Student Sheet 10b: Anchor Activity Schedule, tape it to the inside front cover of your science notebook. You will need to refer to it as you work on the Anchor Activity. Follow it carefully, or you may lose points.

2. Follow along as your teacher reviews the Anchor Activity Guidelines.

MATERIALS FOR LESSON 10

For you

- 1 copy of Student Sheet 10a: What Are Bikes Made From and Why?
- 1 copy of Student Sheet 10b: Anchor Activity Schedule
  Clear tape or glue
  Scissors
  Card stock, poster board, or lightweight cardboard

THE RIGHT MATERIAL

Matter is used to make things. The term "technology" refers to the way people alter and shape matter so that it can be used to make things. For example, gold can be found as metal nuggets. But through technology (for example, the lost wax method), it can be fashioned into jewelry. Through different technology, it can be used to plate electronic components inside a computer.

Part of making any useful object is choosing the right kind of material for it. Materials can be any type of matter, from the metal in a bicycle frame to the compressed air in a bicycle tire. Some materials are used directly from nature (for example, wood and stone). These are called raw materials. Other materials are made from raw materials that are refined or processed in some way. For example, one of the raw materials used to make glass is sand.

What properties made aluminum and transparent plastic ideal materials for the manufacture of this disk?

Think about some everyday manufactured objects. Some are very complex. For example, a car contains thousands of different parts and is made from hundreds of different types of matter. Each material used to build the car is chosen for the job it must do. That job is its function. How is this choice made? It is based on several factors, including cost, availability, and, most important, the properties of the material.

Scientists and engineers are often on the lookout for better, cheaper, or more readily available materials to replace the traditional materials used in objects. They try to find or design materials that have the right properties. For example, most shoes were once made entirely from pieces of leather that were sewn or nailed together. Nowadays, many shoes are made from a variety of materials, each suited or designed to fit the function of that part of the shoe. Soles may consist of a combination of durable, shock-absorbing rubbers or plastics. Uppers are often made of waterproof, breathable synthetic fabrics or stain-resistant plastics with soft linings that cushion the foot and protect from abrasion.

During the Anchor Activity, you will learn more about the materials that make up an object. You will study the relationship between object function, the choice of materials to make the object, and the properties and origins of the materials.

Anchor Activity Guidelines

PROCEDURE

Part 1: Choosing the Object

1. To make your work easier, you and your partner should choose a relatively simple manufactured object. Discuss with your partner which object you are going to research. You do not need to make a final decision immediately. Some examples are given in the list entitled "Anchor Activity Objects." You can choose one of these or think of another that you use every day. But remember, keep the object simple. An object made from two or three materials will be much easier to research and present than one made from many materials.

Anchor Activity Objects

Aerosol can	Ballpoint pen
Battery	Bottle
Cassette tape	CD/DVD
Clothing	Cooking pot
Diaper	Felt-tip pen
Floppy disk	Football
Furniture	Golf ball
In-line skates	Joystick
Knife	Lightbulb
Magnifier	Matches
Notebook	Pencil
Pencil sharpener	Scissors
Sneakers	Soda can
Tape dispenser	Thermometer
Tools	Toothbrush
Toy	Videotape

2. During the next week, meet with your partner and write a short paragraph identifying the object you have chosen. Give the reasons for your choice (Figure 10.1 shows a sample paragraph). Hand it in by the due date on your schedule. Your teacher must approve your object. If too many pairs choose the same object, you may be asked to select another.

Jane Lionel and Juanita Lopez

We have chosen eyeglasses for our piece of research. Both of us wear glasses for reading. We are going to take Juanita's glasses as our example. They are made from three types of substances. Some type of golden metal, they have glass lenses and plastic nose pieces as well as plastic pads on the stems.

Figure 10.1 *Sample paragraph identifying an object and outlining the reason for its choice*

Part 2: Starting the Research

1. Start gathering information about your object. Your information will be divided into five sections. As you gather information, write your notes under these headings:

- **Function** (Explain what the object does or what its use is.)
- **Major Materials** (Give the main materials from which the object is made.)
- **Why These Materials Were Chosen** (Tell what properties of the materials make them good choices for use in the object.)
- **Origin of One of the Materials** (Select one major material in the object and investigate its raw materials, where they are found, and the processes they undergo to make them usable in the object.)
- **History of the Object** (Answer these questions: Was it invented? If so, by whom? When and where did it first appear? How do the original designs and choice of materials differ from those in use today?)

2. The section "Origin of One of the Materials" is similar to (but not as detailed as) the topic of your oral presentation. See Part 4: Giving the Oral Presentation (on page 95) to find out what you should research for your presentation.

3. Use your notes to help you conduct a brainstorming session with your partner. After the brainstorming session, write an outline of your investigation. The outline should be in a format similar to that shown in Figure 10.2.

Figure 10.2 *Example of an outline of Anchor Activity research*

4. On another sheet of paper, write a bibliography. The bibliography can include books, newspapers, magazines, and TV programs. You should have at least one Internet and one CD-ROM or DVD reference (see Figure 10.3).

5. Hand in your outline and bibliography on or before the due date on your schedule. Your teacher will use this information to make sure your research is heading in the right direction.

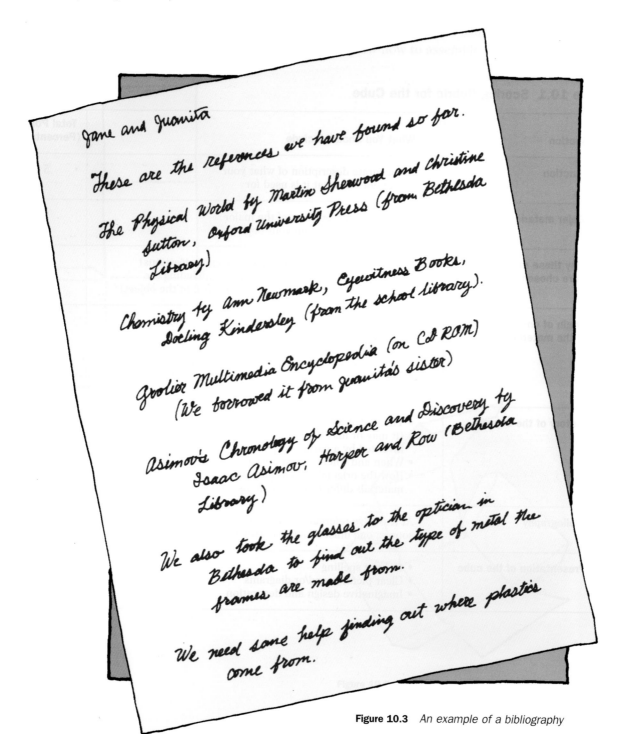

Jane and Juanita

These are the references we have found so far.

The Physical World by Martin Sherwood and Christine Sutton, Oxford University Press (from Bethesda Library)

Chemistry by Ann Newmark, Eyewitness Books, Dorling Kindersley (from the school library).

Grolier Multimedia Encyclopedia (on CD ROM) (We borrowed it from Juanita's sister)

Asimov's Chronology of Science and Discovery by Isaac Asimov, Harper and Row (Bethesda Library)

We also took the glasses to the optician in Bethesda to find out the type of metal the frames are made from.

We need some help finding out where plastics come from.

Figure 10.3 *An example of a bibliography*

6. Use one side of the cube for each section you have written (this will use five sides). Make sure that at least four sides of the cube read the same way up (see Figure 10.6). Put a picture or photograph (or, if possible, the object) on the sixth side. It is important that your names and bibliography appear somewhere on the exhibit. Figures 10.7 and 10.8 show completed cubes.

7. If your cube is too small for all your information to fit, include the additional information in your oral presentation.

8. Hand in your exhibit on or before the due date.

Figure 10.6 *At least four sides of the cube should read the same way up.*

Figure 10.7 *The students who built these cubes had fun researching and decorating them!*

Figure 10.8 *Once complete, the cubes from your class will make an exciting exhibition about materials and how we use them. Although each cube follows the same format, your personal touches will make your cube unique.*

Part 4: Giving the Oral Presentation

1. Work with your partner to prepare a short oral presentation. It should focus on the origin of one of the materials that make up your object. You should provide *detailed* information on the following topics:

   - One of the materials from which your object is made
   - The properties of the material
   - The properties of the material that make it a good choice for use in your object
   - One of the raw materials from which the material is made
   - The geographical source or sources of the raw material
   - How the raw material is extracted and/or processed before it is used in your object

2. Both you and your partner should be involved in giving the presentation. During your presentation, use some visual aids such as posters, maps, and overhead transparencies. If you can, use Web pages or a short video.

3. Carefully read Table 10.2. It tells you how your oral presentation will be assessed. Use the table to plan your presentation.

4. With your partner, practice giving the presentation. Time yourselves so that the presentation is between 3 and 5 minutes long.

5. Make sure you have all of your materials ready before you give your presentation. You may refer to notes during your presentation, but you should avoid reading them.

Table 10.2 Scoring Rubric for the Oral Presentation

Component	What You Should Include	Total Points (Percentage)
Content	Detailed descriptions of the following: • One of the materials from which your object is made • The properties of the material • The properties of the material that make it a good choice for use in your object • One of the raw materials from which the material is made • The geographical source or sources of the raw material • How the raw material is extracted and/or processed before use in your object	10
Presentation and use of visual aids	• Speaking loudly and clearly • Appropriate visual aids for your presentation • Visual aids large enough to be read from the back of the room	10
Organization	• A short introduction, main section, and a conclusion or short summary • Equal contribution by you and your partner	10

What Is Each Part of the Anchor Activity Worth?

The completion of each item listed on the Anchor Activity Schedule by its due date is worth 15 percent of your total grade for the Anchor Activity; the cube is worth 55 percent; and the oral presentation is worth 30 percent.

When Will You Do All of This Work?

You will be given several homework assignments and a small amount of class time to do this work. However, you will have to do most of it on your own time. At the end of the module, two to three class periods will be used for the Anchor Activity presentations.

BICYCLE INGREDIENTS

AP/WIDE WORLD PHOTOS

Bicycles like this one, made partially from carbon composites, are lighter than metal bikes and can be designed to be more aerodynamic than those made from metals.

Compared to cars, bicycles look pretty simple. But this appearance is deceiving. Even an inexpensive bike can be made of more than a hundred different materials. These include several kinds of steel, other metals such as chrome and aluminum, several kinds of rubber, a few oils, and different types of plastic.

Dan Connors is an engineer with Cannondale Corporation, a company in Connecticut that makes bikes. He says choosing the material for each bicycle part always boils down to a trade-off between strength, weight, and price. "You want all the parts to be strong, but they can't weigh too much. Nobody wants to pedal around with a bunch of excess weight," he says. But price is important, too. "You can design the greatest thing in the world. But if that means putting a thousand dollar part on a bike you want to sell for five hundred bucks, you won't get too far," Connors says.

The single biggest part of a bicycle is

the frame. The first bike frames were made of wood.

Today, most bike frames are made of steel. Steel has a good balance between strength and weight. It is easy to work with. It also doesn't cost much. For more expensive frames, designers often choose aluminum. Aluminum or aluminum alloys can have the same strength as steel, but they weigh less. Aluminum is also cheap to buy. Unfortunately, it is tricky to weld aluminum pieces together, so aluminum frames cost more.

Some very high-priced bikes have frames made of carbon composites. These new materials are made by setting strong carbon fibers in a solid plastic matrix. Frames made of carbon composite can be as strong as steel but weigh only one-third as much, says Connors.

Strength, weight, and cost are important for other parts of a bike, too. Take the gears, for example. The big front gear

Modern bikes are composed of varied materials.

Grips: Vinyl elastomer

Brakepads: Rubber (sometimes with asbestos added)

Seat: Chrome, molybdenum, and steel rails; vinyl cover, silicon elastomer cushioning

Frame: Aluminum

Rim: Aluminum

Spokes: Stainless steel

Rear derailleur: Glass-reinforced nylon jockey wheels

Tires: Rubber with fiber reinforcement

turned by the pedals does not need to be as strong as the gears on the back wheel. Designers often save a little weight by using aluminum alloy for the front gear, says Connors, but this trick won't work at the back. "You might save a little weight if you put aluminum alloy gears in the back, but the gears would wear out after a couple of months," he says. The back gears are usually made from more durable steel.

Tires are made of rubber. Rubber is flexible and holds air, but by itself, it is not very strong. To compensate

The draisienne, invented in 1818, was the first two-wheeled machine for personal transport. It had no pedals and was made from iron and wood, the most practical materials available at that time.

for the lack of strength of rubber, bicycle tire makers embed long fibers, often made from nylon, inside the rubber. The fibers help the tire hold its shape and resist punctures.

The ball bearings inside the axles of the wheels are especially hardened steel. They may be sealed with lubricants that have special additives to withstand heat.

You might think that it would be very difficult to improve on something that has been around for more than a hundred years, like the bicycle. Fortunately, new materials are constantly being discovered or invented. This gives engineers like Dan Connors new options for designing bicycles. □

11
Pure Substance or Mixture?

CORBIS/PHILIP GOULD

Milk looks like a single substance.
Is it pure or is it a mixture?

INTRODUCTION

In previous lessons, you discovered how the characteristics of substances, such as density, and the behavior of substances when they are heated can be used to help identify substances. However, there is one problem. These properties are most useful in identifying pure substances. Many of the materials that we come across in our daily lives are not pure. Mixtures of substances are much more common than pure substances are. For example, look at your own body. You are made up of matter that consists of many complex substances that work together to produce the chemical reactions that occur in living organisms (see Figure 11.1).

OBJECTIVES FOR THIS LESSON

Discuss the meaning of the term "pure substance."

Discuss how you can distinguish between pure substances and mixtures.

Use your own techniques to discover whether several samples of matter are pure substances or mixtures.

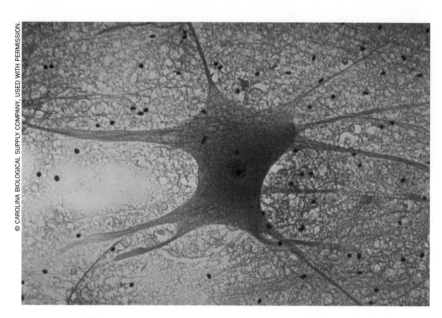

Figure 11.1 *This nerve cell, like every cell in your body, contains thousands of different substances. Each one performs a different function within the cell.*

Identifying the individual substances from which living things are made is very difficult. To separate the substances in a living cell, a biochemist would need to grind up samples of the tissue and then expose the souplike mixture to an array of separation techniques to obtain pure samples of each substance.

Finding out whether something is pure is hard work! In this lesson, you will try to define the term "pure substance." You will devise your own techniques to determine whether eight different samples are pure substances or mixtures. You will then discuss the difficulties you encountered in classifying the samples.

MATERIALS FOR LESSON 11

For you

1 copy of Student Sheet 11.1: Identifying Pure Substances and Mixtures

1 pair of safety goggles

For your group

8 samples (labeled A through H)

4 loupes (double-eye magnifiers)

2 lab scoops

2 pipettes

4 petri dish lids or bases

4 sheets of black paper

4 sheets of white paper

1 magnet

4 test tubes

1 test tube rack

1 test tube brush

Access to water

Getting Started

1. Before you start investigating whether substances are pure or mixtures, it would be useful to think about how you already use these terms. Answer the following questions on your student sheet: What is your definition of a pure substance? Give two examples of pure substances. For each, explain why you think it is pure. If you were given an unknown sample of matter, how could you tell whether it was a pure substance or a mixture?

2. Use your answers to contribute to a class discussion.

SAFETY TIPS

Wear your safety goggles throughout the inquiry.

Do not taste any of the substances.

Inquiry 11.1
Determining Whether Substances Are Pure or Mixtures

PROCEDURE

1. Have one member of your group collect the plastic box of materials. Check its contents against the list of materials.

2. Take samples A through H out of the plastic box.

3. The purpose of this inquiry is to answer the question, "Which of these substances are mixtures and which are pure substances?" You have about 20 minutes to answer this question and to record your answers, so you will need to split the work among the members of your group.

4. You may use all of the apparatus in the plastic box, plus water, to help you with your investigation. Devise your own techniques to determine whether each sample is a pure substance or a mixture.

5. For each sample, record your findings in Table 1 on the student sheet.

6. Use any additional data collected by other group members to complete Table 1. Discuss the results with the other members of your group.

7. Answer the following questions on your student sheet: How can the properties of pure substances be used to discover whether a sample is a mixture? Were the samples all well mixed? How did the extent of mixing affect your investigation?

8. Put the wastes from Mixtures G and H in the appropriate container. Wash all of the test tubes and return the materials to the plastic box. Make sure you also wash your hands when you are finished.

9. Your teacher will lead a class discussion about your procedures and results. Listen carefully as other students describe their approaches to answering the question of whether a sample is a pure substance or a mixture, explain their results, and make suggestions for alternative approaches to the problem.

REFLECTING ON WHAT YOU'VE DONE

1. After the discussion, your teacher will return to the concept of "pure substance." Look at the definition you provided at the start of the lesson.

2. Review your original definition of "pure substance." If it is different from the new one agreed on in class, write the new one on the student sheet.

Perfect Teamwork

Wouldn't it be great to have a baseball team made entirely of the world's greatest pitchers? Well, no. This would not be a happy team. It wouldn't matter how many strikes these superstars could throw. A team without players who are good at catching, hitting, and stealing bases would have a hard time winning. A team with a good balance of skills is more likely to make it to the World Series.

Combining skills is important for making strong materials, too. Often, a pure substance on its own does not have all of the necessary properties for a particular material. But you can make many useful materials by combining two or more substances that have different properties. The result is a mixture called a composite. A good composite exploits the best properties of each ingredient.

People have been making composites since the beginning of civilization. For ancient peoples, dried mud and even animal dung were handy for making huts. The huts were simple to make: Find dirt, add water. The mud kept out the wind and didn't rot, but it crumbled and cracked. Ancient peoples also used straw, grass, or sticks, which were woven into durable mats, to make hut walls. But woven walls leaked.

The solution was to combine the two. In many parts of the world, people realized they could weave a house frame (usually supported by timber) out of straw, grass, or sticks and cover it with mud. The result, called "wattle-and-daub" construction, wasn't always pretty. But it kept out the cold and did not fall apart every time the kids got a little rowdy.

People have been coming up with new composite materials ever since. Usually, a composite has two materials with opposite properties. The two materials put together as a composite can do what each ingredient alone cannot. Like ancient wattle-and-daub huts, modern composites are often made of fibers embedded in a solid that sticks the fibers together. The fibers are strong but floppy. The solid isn't floppy, but it easily shatters or cracks. A combination of these two opposites can be unbeatable.

The Masai of Kenya have been using composite materials— mud, dung, and straw—to make homes for thousands of years.

PHOTO BY BRIAN O'KEEFE

Why are fiberglass and carbon fiber composites good materials for making fishing rods?

The solid provides stiffness. The fibers keep the solid from cracking apart. (This is because a crack would have to break too many of the strong fibers running through the solid.)

Fiberglass is one example of a modern composite. To make fiberglass, glass is melted and stretched into long threads. The glass threads are woven into cloth. The cloth is embedded in plastic goo, and the whole thing is shaped in a mold. When the goo hardens, the object has the shape of the mold, is light in weight, and is cheap to make. Fiberglass was originally developed to cover radar dishes on World War II bombers. It is now used for everything from boats to fishing rods to picnic tables.

PHOTO COURTESY OF U.S. NAVY BLUE ANGELS

Navy Blue Angels fly F/A-18 Hornets with composite wings.

When building the Stealth Fighter, designers used many composite materials in place of metal. The use of these materials combined with its special shape helps make the plane invisible to most radar.

More recently, engineers have developed new composite materials. One of these composites contains carbon fibers that are stiffer and much more heat-resistant than glass is. A given weight of carbon composite is stronger than steel. This lightweight strength makes carbon composites ideal for use in many types of objects that would normally be made of metal. The wings of jet fighter planes and helicopter blades are two examples.

Composites are widely used in sports equipment and are replacing many natural materials. For example, tennis rackets, originally made from wood, now have frames made from glass, carbon, or boron fibers embedded in a plastic-like nylon. The core of the racket is made from a plastic foam. The result is a lightweight, stiff racket that is easy to control and that returns the ball with maximum force.

Even though carbon composites are one of the latest advances in composite materials, they share something with ancient mud huts. Both combine the best parts of different materials to make something that is better than either one alone. □

About 50 years ago, solid wooden rackets were used to play tennis.

QUESTIONS

1. What is one object made from a composite material that you can find in your home?
2. What is the function of the object?
3. Why was that composite material chosen for that function?

Modern rackets like this one, made from several types of composites, are much stronger and lighter than wooden rackets.

12

What Happens When Substances Are Mixed With Water?

Why doesn't the sand on this beach mix easily with the water in this lake?

INTRODUCTION

What happens when different substances are mixed with water? Do they all behave in the same way? Does the type of mixture that a substance forms with water depend on the properties of the substance? In this lesson, you will investigate what happens when you mix several pure substances with water. Using your observations, you will identify some of the characteristics of solutions. You will also discuss the terms that are used to describe the formation of solutions.

OBJECTIVES FOR THIS LESSON

Make observations of what happens when different substances are mixed with water.

Identify the characteristics of solutions.

Define and use some terms that describe the parts of a solution and the processes that take place when solutions are formed.

Getting Started

1. Your group will be given a test tube containing a mixture of food coloring and water. In your science notebook, write all the properties of this mixture that you can observe.

2. The class will discuss these observations and relate them to the mixtures you will investigate in this lesson.

3. Return the tube of food coloring to your teacher. Keep the beaker; you can use it to collect water for Inquiry 12.1.

SAFETY TIPS

Wear safety goggles throughout the lesson.

If you splash a solution in your eyes, immediately flush out your eyes with a lot of water and report the accident to your teacher.

Do not mix the contents of different test tubes.

When you complete the inquiry, wash your hands.

MATERIALS FOR LESSON 12

For you
- 1 copy of Student Sheet 12.1: Mixing Substances With Water
- 1 pair of safety goggles

For you and your lab partner
- 1 test tube rack
- 5 test tubes
- 2 rubber stoppers
- 1 lab scoop
- 1 metric ruler
- 1 test tube brush
  Access to water

For your group
- 5 jars containing these substances:
    Copper (II) sulfate
    Sodium chloride
    Zinc oxide
    Sulfur
    Confectioners' sugar
- 1 plastic cup
- 1 label

Inquiry 12.1
Adding Water to Substances

PROCEDURE

1. In Inquiry 12.1, you will work in pairs, but you will discuss your results with the other members of your group.

2. One person from your group should collect a plastic box containing the materials. Check the contents of the plastic box against the materials list. You will be sharing the jars containing the substances and the plastic cup with other members of your group, but make sure your pair has one set of the remaining apparatus.

3. You have samples of five different substances. You are going to investigate what happens to each of them when you add water to them.

4. Put one lab scoop of copper (II) sulfate into a test tube.

5. Add water to a depth of 5 cm.

6. Seal the test tube with a rubber stopper.

7. Shake the mixture 10 times. Do not knock the tube against the desk.

8. Examine the contents of the tube (see Figure 12.1). Observe what happens to the solid substance you put in the tube. Write the name of the substance in Table 1 on Student Sheet 12.1. Describe the appearance of the contents in the appropriate space in the table.

9. Repeat the procedure with the remaining four substances.

10. Discuss your results with the other members of your group. Complete the third column of Table 1.

11. Label the plastic cup with the names of the members of your group. Pour the two test tubes of copper (II) sulfate solution into the plastic cup. Store the cup in a safe, warm place. You will look at it again in Lesson 15.

12. Do not clean up your remaining materials until after the class discussion. Put the zinc oxide waste into the container provided. Wash the sulfur down the drain with a lot of water.

Figure 12.1 *Look at your mixture. Is it transparent? Is it of uniform composition? Is it a solution?*

REFLECTING ON WHAT YOU'VE DONE

1. Discuss the results of Inquiry 12.1 with the rest of the class.

2. Observe carefully as your teacher shows you what happens when water is added to potassium permanganate. After the demonstration, write on the student sheet a full description of what happened. Use the terms that have been discussed during the lesson. Look at the terms listed in Step 4 of this section if you are unsure what these words are.

3. Your teacher will repeat the demonstration using sand. Describe your observations as before.

4. On the student sheet, write your definitions of the following terms: soluble, insoluble, solvent, solute, solution, and dissolve.

5. Clean your apparatus and return it to the plastic box.

Dissolving History

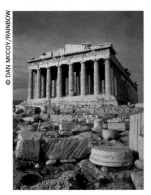

The Parthenon stands with other ancient buildings on the Acropolis, which overlooks the city of Athens. These buildings have survived for thousands of years. However, air pollution, caused mainly by motor vehicle exhaust, has greatly damaged them.

Dateline: January 1998, Athens, Greece

A team of archaeologists, architects, iron-workers, and marble cutters has just started a new project. Its goal? To restore the Temple of Athena, a masterpiece of Greek architecture that was built in the fifth century B.C. The surface of the historic monument has been deteriorating for decades. It's time for temple-saving action.

The workers know that they have a hard job ahead. Work on another famous Greek temple, the Parthenon, has been going on for nearly 60 years, and it's not done yet.

These buildings, like many monuments, are built of marble—one of the hardest stones. Why are they in need of restoration?

Wind and rain have always had an effect on buildings, but the main cause of deterioration is pollution. The problem is not just in Athens. In cities around the world, historic buildings are literally being dissolved away.

The major culprits are acid rain and smog (visible as a reddish brown haze), which is a problem in most of the world's large cities. Both originate with the burning of fossil fuels, such as coal and petroleum. As these fuels burn, they give off gases, which include the pollutants sulfur dioxide and nitrogen oxides. One major source of nitrogen oxides is auto exhaust fumes. Sulfur dioxide is produced in particularly large quantities by coal-burning

Much of the damage caused to the Parthenon is the result of the action of acid rain dissolving the marble from which it was built.

power plants and other industrial operations.

These gases rise into the atmosphere, where they combine with oxygen and water vapor. The sulfur dioxide becomes sulfuric acid, and the nitric oxides become nitric acid. Together, they form an acid solution that falls to earth as acid rain (or acid sleet or snow).

All rain is slightly acidic, but acid rain does much more damage to buildings. It is especially harmful to buildings made from rocks that contain calcium carbonate or magnesium carbonate. Marble, used in many Athenian buildings, and the softer, even more vulnerable, limestone both contain carbonates. As years pass, the acid solution reacts with the surfaces of monuments and buildings and turns them into soluble substances. Acid rain can also attack paint and metals, and it forms a crust on the surface of glass.

Not only does acid rain harm buildings, it damages trees and kills aquatic life and other organisms. To fight these effects, people around the world are applying a great deal of ingenuity to solve the problem of acid rain. In many countries, fossil-fuel-burning power plants and other industrial plants now remove some acidic gases from the waste products that would otherwise be dispersed through smokestacks. Also, special devices are being fitted to car tailpipes to remove some of these gases from exhaust fumes.

This steelworks is belching out smoke and gases, including those that cause acid rain. Pollution as bad as this is no longer allowed in the United States, but it is still common in some other countries of the world.

Despite improved regulation of emissions, motor vehicles are a major source of the air pollution that causes acid rain.

Until the source of the pollution is completely removed, any efforts to restore ancient buildings will be only stopgap measures. The team of workers on the Acropolis in Athens, in other words, is dealing with the symptoms, but not the cure. ☐

Acid rain has dissolved parts of these statues.

What Can You Do About Acid Rain?

- Use the car less. Carpool, use public transportation, ride a bike, or walk.
- Conserve electricity. Most electricity is produced by coal-burning power plants, and coal emits a high amount of sulfur when it burns.
- Study historical sites, buildings, or cemetery headstones in your area. Try to find out how they have been affected by acid rain.
- Contact a local environmental group to see whether it has taken action about acid rain.

QUESTION

How is acid rain formed? Write a short paragraph describing this process.

How Much Solute Dissolves in a Solvent?

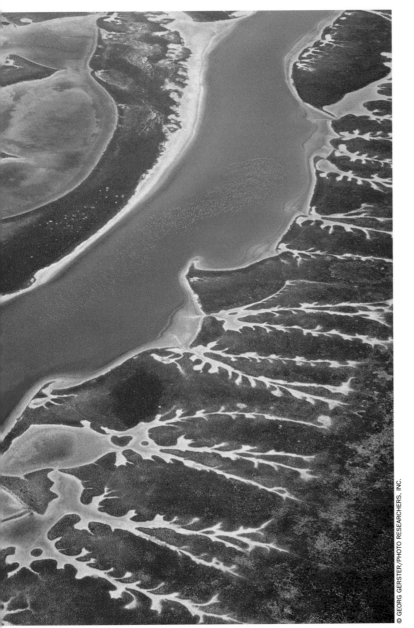

Solid soluble salt and water are seen next to each other in this lake in Namibia, Africa. How can solid soluble salt and water exist in the same place?

© GEORG GERSTER/PHOTO RESEARCHERS, INC.

INTRODUCTION

As you know from Lesson 12, solutions are made from solvents and solutes. When you add a spoonful of common salt (sodium chloride) to a pan of water, it dissolves. Salt is soluble in water. Add a second spoonful, and that also dissolves. But what would happen if you kept adding salt? Would it continue to dissolve? Could you add more salt than there was water, or would the salt eventually stop dissolving? What would happen if you used a soluble substance other than salt? Would the same amount of that substance dissolve? These are some of the questions you will try to answer in this lesson. You will start by examining a blue liquid and explaining your observations of the liquid on the basis of what you already know. You will then investigate two white crystalline substances. One is sodium chloride, and the other is sodium nitrate. They look almost the same, but as you will discover, they have different characteristics when they are added to water. Could these different characteristics be used to help identify these two substances?

OBJECTIVES FOR THIS LESSON

Make solutions using different amounts of solute.

Discover what is meant by the term "saturated solution."

With your class, design and conduct an experiment to determine the solubility of two different substances.

Discuss the design of your inquiry.

Discuss solubility as a characteristic property of matter.

Getting Started

1. One student from your group should collect the plastic box containing the materials.

2. Take out the test tube rack and the test tube containing the blue liquid. Pass the test tube around your group so that each member of your group can examine it closely. Discuss with other members of your group precisely what you observe in the tube. Write your observations in your science notebook. What can you conclude from your observations?

3. Participate in a class discussion of your observations.

4. Before proceeding with Inquiry 13.1, hand in the test tube containing the blue liquid. Clean the remaining test tube. Return the test tube rack to the plastic box.

SAFETY TIP

Wear your safety goggles at all times.

MATERIALS FOR LESSON 13

For you
- 1 copy of Student Sheet 13.1: Saturating a Solution
- 1 copy of Student Sheet 13.2: Determining Solubility
- 1 pair of safety goggles

For you and your lab partner
- 1 100-mL graduated cylinder
- 2 test tubes
- 1 test tube rack
- 2 rubber stoppers
- 1 lab scoop
- 1 jar containing sodium chloride
- 1 jar containing sodium nitrate
  Access to an electronic balance

For your group
- 1 test tube containing a blue liquid

Inquiry 13.1
Saturating a Solution

PROCEDURE

1. Check the materials in your plastic box against the materials list, and divide them equally between the two pairs in your group.

2. How much salt (sodium chloride) can you get to dissolve in a test tube filled halfway with water? Fill one test tube halfway with water. Add one level lab scoop of salt to the test tube. Shake the mixture to help the salt dissolve faster. If it completely dissolves, add more salt. Keep adding salt until no more dissolves.

3. Answer the following questions on Student Sheet 13.1: How many scoops of sodium chloride dissolved in the water? How did you know that no more would dissolve?

4. After a short class discussion, write your definition of a saturated solution on the student sheet.

5. Think about how you could adapt the technique you used in Step 2 to find out how many grams of sodium chloride dissolved in water.

6. Rinse the test tube with water. Put the test tube in the test tube rack.

Inquiry 13.2
Determining Solubility

PROCEDURE

1. Using the apparatus you have been given, how could you compare how much of each of the two substances (sodium nitrate and sodium chloride) will dissolve in water? Here are some questions you need to discuss with your partner:

   A. *What will you need to measure?*

   B. *How will you know when you have a saturated solution?*

   C. *How will you calculate the amount dissolved?*

2. Your teacher will conduct a short brainstorming session. Be prepared to contribute to the discussion. By the end of the brainstorming session, the class will have agreed on a procedure for determining solubility.

3. Answer the following questions on Student Sheet 13.2: What are you trying to find out? What materials will you use? What is your procedure?

4. Under Step 4 of Student Sheet 13.2, design a data table to record your results and calculations.

5. Follow the class procedure for determining solubility, and record your results in the data table. When you have finished, pour the solutions down the drain with lots of water. Clean the test tubes and return the materials to the plastic box.

6. Under Step 5 on the student sheet, calculate the number of grams of each substance that dissolved in the water and answer the following question: Are the different substances equally soluble in water?

7. Under Step 6 on the student sheet, write any problems you had with the experiment or the approach and answer the following question: Could any of these problems have affected your results?

REFLECTING ON WHAT YOU'VE DONE

1. You will have an opportunity to look at the results of other pairs. Be prepared to discuss how these results could give a more accurate measure of the solubility of these two substances.

2. Answer the following question on Student Sheet 13.2: How could you use the property of solubility to help you identify a type of matter?

3. Read "Solubility and Saturated Solutions."

SOLUBILITY AND SATURATED SOLUTIONS

At room temperature, a solvent (such as water) can dissolve only a certain amount of solute. For example, in Inquiry 13.1, after adding a few lab scoops of sodium chloride to the water, you could see a white solid (undissolved sodium chloride) at the bottom of the tube. The white solid indicated that the water could not dissolve any more sodium chloride. When this happens, the solution is called saturated. The mass of solute dissolved in a given volume or mass of a solvent is its solubility. Solubility is usually measured in grams of solute per unit volume of solvent (for example, grams per liter) or in grams per 100 g of solvent.

The solubility of a solute changes with changing temperature. For example, sodium nitrate becomes more soluble as the temperature rises. It is about twice as soluble at 80 °C as it is at 1 °C. There are some substances that become less soluble as the temperature rises. When you heated water in Lesson 7, you may have noticed that bubbles appeared, even though the water was well below the boiling point. These were bubbles of gases, such as oxygen and nitrogen, that were dissolved in the water. The gases became less soluble as the water was heated, and they were released from solution.

14

Mass, Volume, and Dissolving

What happens to the mass of a solute when the solute is added to a solvent?

ANNE WILLIAMS/NSRC

INTRODUCTION

What happens to the mass and volume of two substances when the substances are mixed to form a solution? Will the mass and volume of the solute and the solvent remain the same before and after dissolving? In this lesson, you will conduct two inquiries. In the first inquiry, you will make a solution from two liquids of known mass and volume and compare their masses and volumes before and after mixing. In the second inquiry, you and your lab partner will devise a procedure for determining whether any change in mass occurs when salt (sodium chloride) is dissolved in water.

OBJECTIVES FOR THIS LESSON

Predict what happens to the mass and volume of a solute and a solvent when these substances are mixed together to form a solution.

Perform an inquiry to test your predictions.

Design and conduct an inquiry to investigate whether a change in mass occurs when sodium chloride dissolves in water.

Getting Started

1. Previously in the module, you learned that two properties of matter are mass and volume. Why is mass, and not volume, used to measure the amount of matter in an object? Discuss this question with the other members of your group. You will be expected to contribute your ideas to a class discussion about mass and volume.

2. One member of your group should collect the plastic box containing the materials. Check the contents of the plastic box against the materials list.

3. You will be working in pairs. Split the apparatus equally between the pairs in your group.

4. Fill the beaker with water. You will use this water to practice pouring an exact volume of water into a 100-mL graduated cylinder.

5. With your partner, review and practice the correct technique (refer to Figure 2.2 in Lesson 2 and Figure 14.1 in this lesson to ensure an accurate measurement), as follows:

A. One partner chooses an exact volume of water for the other partner to pour into the graduated cylinder.

For you

- 1 copy of Student Sheet 14.1: Mixing Water and Alcohol
- 1 copy of Student Sheet 14.2: Dissolving a Solid and Measuring Mass
- 1 pair of safety goggles

For your group

- 2 250-mL beakers
- 4 100-mL graduated cylinders
- 2 pipettes
- 4 test tubes
- 2 lab scoops
- 2 jars containing sodium chloride
- 2 bottles containing ethyl alcohol (ethanol)
- 4 paper towels
  Access to water
  Access to an electronic balance

B. Place the graduated cylinder on a level surface.

C. Fill the graduated cylinder to 1.0 or 2.0 mL below the volume you require.

D. Using the pipette, slowly add water until you have the exact volume you want.

6. Carefully check your partner's measurement.

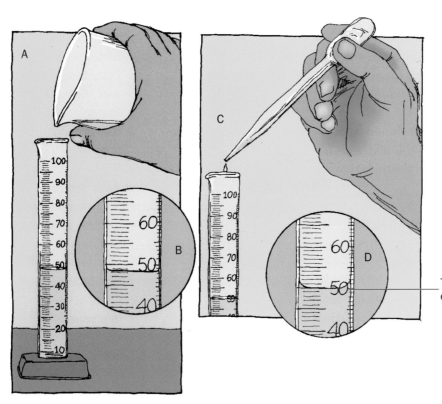

The bottom of the meniscus aligns exactly on the measurement you want.

Figure 14.1 *(A) Place the cylinder on a level surface. (B) Fill the cylinder to within 1.0 or 2.0 mL of the volume you want. (C) Slowly add water, using the pipette, until (D) the meniscus aligns exactly at the volume you want.*

Inquiry 14.1
Mixing Water and Alcohol

PROCEDURE

1. Put exactly 50.0 mL of water into one of the 100-mL graduated cylinders.

2. Put exactly 50.0 mL of ethyl alcohol into the other 100-mL graduated cylinder.

3. Measure the mass of each cylinder and its contents. Record your results in Table 1 on Student Sheet 14.1.

4. Predict what you think the volume will be after you mix the water and the ethyl alcohol. Predict what you think the mass will be after you mix the water and the ethyl alcohol.

5. Record your predictions in Table 1.

6. Test your predictions by carefully pouring the ethyl alcohol into the 100-mL cylinder containing the water (see Figure 14.2). Allow a minute for the ethyl alcohol to drain completely from the graduated cylinder. Gently tap the cylinder with your finger to speed up the process. Take care to avoid spills.

Figure 14.2 *Carefully mix the two liquids. Allow a minute for the ethyl alcohol to drain completely from the cylinder. Gently tap the cylinder with your finger to speed up the process. Take care to avoid spills.*

7. Measure the volume of the mixture. Measure the combined mass of both of the graduated cylinders and the mixture. In Table 1, record your measurements and calculate any differences in mass and volume before and after mixing. Empty the graduated cylinder.

8. Answer the following questions on the student sheet: What type of mixture was formed when you mixed the water and the ethyl alcohol? What happened to the volume? What happened to the mass?

9. Write your results in the class results table (on the board or transparency).

10. Compare your results with those of the rest of the class. What conclusions can you reach? Write your answer on the student sheet. Be prepared to explain your conclusions during a class discussion.

11. Put the ethanol-water mixture in the appropriate container.

Inquiry 14.2
Dissolving a Solid and Measuring Mass

PROCEDURE

1. You and your lab partner will design an inquiry to determine what happens to the mass of sodium chloride and water when sodium chloride is dissolved in water. The following questions may help you in the design process:

A. What do you need to measure?

B. What apparatus should you use? (You may use any of the materials that are in the plastic box.)

C. How much solute and solvent will you use? (Remember to consider the solubility of the sodium chloride.)

D. What precautions should you take to obtain accurate measurements?

E. How will you record your results?

2. Write your procedure on Student Sheet 14.2. If you have any problems, discuss them with your teacher.

3. Conduct the inquiry.

4. Record your results on the student sheet. Compare them with those obtained by other pairs.

5. Clean and dry your apparatus. Return it to the plastic box.

6. What can you conclude from this experiment? Write your answer on the student sheet.

7. Participate in a class discussion about the procedure you used, your results, and your conclusions.

REFLECTING ON WHAT YOU'VE DONE

Answer these questions in your science notebook:

A. What have you discovered by doing these two inquiries?

B. What happens to the mass of two types of matter when they are mixed together to form a solution (for example, when a solid is dissolved in a liquid)?

C. Does the same rule apply to volume?

D. How do your results compare with what you already know about what happens to the mass and volume of matter during phase change?

Separating a Soluble and an Insoluble Substance

Sewage is a mixture. Why is knowledge of separation techniques important to ensure the health of our rivers?

© TOM STACK/TOM STACK & ASSOCIATES

INTRODUCTION

Sewage is very smelly stuff. It is also an interesting mixture. It usually looks like a cloudy brown liquid with lumps floating in it. It is difficult to believe that after it is processed in a sewage facility, it can be released as a clear liquid into a river that is the source of drinking water. Cleaning sewage is a complex process. Workers in treatment facilities apply scientific knowledge of the different properties of the substances found in sewage to remove them from the water. Many types of separation techniques and treatments are involved. Some of the large pieces are removed by a screen. Some of the smaller particles are removed by allowing them to settle out. Other particles are filtered out. Chemicals are added to speed up the cleaning process, and microorganisms are cultivated to eat some of the sewage. Separation techniques play a big part in keeping our rivers clean and a big part in our lives in general. In this lesson, you will apply your knowledge of solutions, separation techniques, and the phases of matter to a separation problem—happily, not the separation of sewage!

OBJECTIVES FOR THIS LESSON

Discuss evaporation as a separation technique.

Filter mixtures containing water.

Design and conduct an inquiry to clean rock salt.

Getting Started

1. One member of your group should collect the plastic box containing the materials. Another student should collect your group's plastic cup from Lesson 12.

2. Use a magnifying loupe to examine the contents of the plastic cup.

3. Discuss the following questions with the other members of your group:

A. What do you think this blue substance is?

B. How did it get there?

C. Where did the water go?

4. Your teacher will ask you about your ideas and observations and will discuss the processes involved in forming the crystals.

5. Predict what will happen to the crystals if you add 25 mL of water to the cup.

6. Test your prediction by adding 25 mL of water to the cup. Use the plastic spoon to stir the contents.

SAFETY TIP

Wear your safety goggles at all times.

MATERIALS FOR LESSON 15

For you

1 copy of Student Sheet 15.1: Filtering a Solution

1 copy of Student Sheet 15.2: Cleaning Rock Salt

1 pair of safety goggles

For your group

Plastic cup from Lesson 12 (labeled with the names of your group)

1 plastic cup

1 jar containing rock salt

1 jar containing zinc oxide

2 funnels

6 filter papers

2 100-mL graduated cylinders

2 lab scoops

2 loupes (double-eye magnifiers)

4 test tubes

2 test tube racks

2 250-mL beakers

2 plastic spoons

7. Think about the answers to the following questions:

A. What happens after you add 25 mL of water to the blue crystals?

B. What are the properties of the mixture?

C. What do you think you have made?

Be prepared to participate in a class discussion.

8. Divide your solution into approximately two equal parts. For the remainder of the lesson, you will work with your lab partner. Divide the apparatus in the plastic box between the two pairs in your group.

Inquiry 15.1
Filtering a Solution

PROCEDURE

1. Your teacher will show you how to fold a piece of filter paper and insert it into a filter funnel. As shown in this demonstration and in Figure 15.1, fold the paper and fit it inside the filter funnel. Wet the paper with a few drops of water so that it sticks to the funnel walls. Observe whether the water passes through the filter paper.

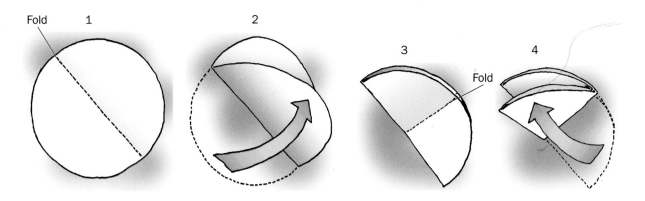

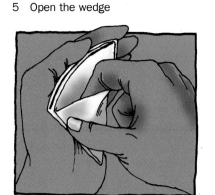

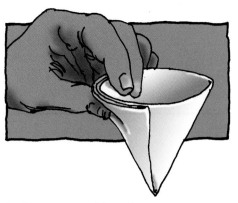

Place the cone in a funnel and wet it with a few drops of clean water

Figure 15.1 *Preparing the filter paper and funnel*

2. What do you think will happen to the copper(II) sulfate solution if you pour it into the funnel? Record your prediction in Table 1 on Student Sheet 15.1.

3. Place a test tube in the test tube rack. Place the funnel with the filter paper into the test tube (see Figure 15.2).

4. Test your prediction by pouring the solution into the funnel. Make sure the solution does not go over the edge of the paper. Record your result in Table 1.

5. Dispose of the filter paper. Fold a new one and place it in the filter funnel.

6. Add one lab scoop of zinc oxide to approximately 10 mL of water in a 250-mL beaker. Stir the mixture with a teaspoon. What will happen when you filter this mixture? Record your prediction in Table 1.

7. Use a clean test tube to repeat the filtration procedure. Record your result in Table 1.

8. Discuss your observations with your partner. What effect did filtration have on the two mixtures? Can you think of another property (other than clearness and uniformity of color) of solutions? Be prepared to participate in a class discussion of your results and to explain your ideas.

9. Use the plastic containers provided to dispose of the copper (II) sulfate solution and the zinc oxide solution. Place your used filter papers in the trash can. Rinse the apparatus and return it to the plastic box.

Figure 15.2 *After setting up your apparatus, pour the copper (II) sulfate solution into the funnel containing the filter paper.*

Inquiry 15.2
Cleaning Rock Salt

PROCEDURE

1. Put four lab scoops of rock salt into the plastic cup. Examine it with the magnifying loupe. Write a description of the rock salt on Student Sheet 15.2.

2. Most of the salt used in food is made from rock salt. Discuss these questions with your partner:

A. *Would you want to eat this sample?*

B. *Do you think it is pure?*

C. *What do you think the contaminants could be?*

3. How could you use the remaining apparatus you have been given to obtain only the soluble component of the rock salt? Record your answers to the following questions on Student Sheet 15.2: What are you trying to do? What materials will you use?

4. On the student sheet, record the procedure devised by you and your partner.

5. Check your ideas with your teacher.

6. Follow your procedure to purify the salt. If you have any problems, consult with your teacher.

You eat this rock. What is it and how is it purified?

REFLECTING ON WHAT YOU'VE DONE

1. Your class will discuss the procedures used by the different pairs.

2. Read "Separating Solids From Liquids."

3. Your cleaned salt sample will not be obtained until a later lesson. When you get a sample of clean solid salt, look at it closely. Are any crystals present? Are they all the same shape? How clean is your salt? Is there any evidence that it is still not pure? If not, can you suggest why?

SEPARATING SOLIDS FROM LIQUIDS

When separating substances, it is important to choose the correct separation technique, which is a method used to separate the components of a mixture from each other. For example, insoluble solids can be separated from liquids in several different ways. The technique used depends on how well substances are mixed together.

To separate insoluble impurities from salt, you used a process called filtration. The filter paper allowed the soluble solute (salt) and the solvent (water) to pass through, but it trapped the larger pieces of insoluble impurities as a residue. The substances that pass through the filter paper are called the filtrate.

Large pieces of insoluble substances will often settle out of a mixture of a solid and a liquid. This process is called sedimentation, because the solid forms a sediment on the bottom of the container. If the solid is very fine, this process can be speeded up with a machine called a centrifuge. Centrifuges spin a test tube very fast, and the solid moves quickly to the bottom of the test tube.

To separate a solid solute from a solvent (like salt from water), you used evaporation. At room temperature, water evaporates from a solution very slowly. But the rate of evaporation can be accelerated by heating the solution. As the water evaporated from your salt and water solution, the solution became more concentrated. Eventually, a saturated solution of salt formed. As more water evaporated, the salt crystallized into white crystals. When crystallization happens slowly, big crystals form. Small crystals form when crystallization happens quickly. Crystalline solids have unique crystal shapes. Therefore, crystal shape is a characteristic property of a substance.

These potassium ferricyanide crystals were produced when the water in a saturated solution of potassium ferricyanide was slowly evaporated.

SEPARATING SOLUTIONS AND THE SALTY SEA

Why is the sea salty? Where does all that salt come from? How does it get there? Much of the salt comes from the land. When it rains, rainwater dissolves soluble substances, including common salt (sodium chloride), from soil and rocks. Some of these substances eventually find their way into creeks and rivers, and from there, they are carried to the sea.

Why is the sea saltier than rivers? Once in the sea, soluble substances are concentrated. Heat from the sun evaporates the water from the sea but leaves the salts behind. Over millions of years, seas become saltier and saltier. For the same reason, lakes that have no outlet to the sea quickly become salty. Lakes can even be saltier than seas are.

Salt is a valuable commodity that has been traded for thousands of years. It is used in food, providing flavor and acting as a food preservative. It is also used to make a wide variety of chemicals. These chemicals are used in many industrial processes, including making glass, soap, and chlorine.

Today, most salt comes from mines, although a lot is also extracted from the sea or salty lake water. Salt has been extracted from salty bodies of water throughout history. One common method of extraction is to let the heat

This caravan of camels is carrying salt across the Sahara Desert to be traded in another part of Africa.

COURTESY OF THE LIBRARY OF CONGRESS

Salt making by evaporation, Salt Lake, Utah (early 20th century).

from the sun completely evaporate seawater that is trapped in pools or small lagoons.

In some desert areas, water is very scarce. But many of these deserts are near seas (or salt lakes), and salt can be removed from seawater to get fresh water. This process is called desalination. Seawater that is desalinated is fresh enough to drink and to grow crops. In some desalination plants, the saltwater is heated. The water evaporates away from the salt, as steam. The steam then condenses to form fresh water. This process requires a lot of energy, so it is very expensive. Other desalination plants remove salt from water by a process called reverse osmosis. □

QUESTIONS

Use library or Internet resources to find information on the locations of the Salton and Aral Seas. Answer the following questions: What do the Salton and Aral Seas have in common? What environmental problems do they have?

PHOTO COURTESY OF US BUREAU OF RECLAMATION

The Yuma Desalting Plant in Arizona is the world's largest desalination plant, capable of producing 72 million gallons of desalted water per day.

LESSON 16
Researching Solvents

This scientist is testing hair products in a consumer test lab. She is using mannequins with real human hair. How do scientists design tests such as this one to make sure they are fair?

INTRODUCTION

How long does a pair of shoes last? How many years does it take for a carpet to wear out? Which toothbrush should I buy? These are typical questions that consumers ask. But where would you look to find the answers? Well, you could try looking in a consumer magazine. These magazines list a range of products—such as cameras, computers, toothbrushes, and household cleaners—and then score them according to how well they work.

Where do the magazines get their information? One approach is to collect details on consumers' experiences with a product. The magazine staff compiles the information to produce a rating. (For example, "Seven out of ten consumers scored the Zippoteeth electric toothbrush the best, while the Scrubboplaque scored the lowest.")

Another, more scientific, approach is to test the products (see Figure 16.1). Each product is put through a series of tests carefully designed to determine how well it does its job. Each product is then given a score using a predetermined scoring system. Results for the electric toothbrushes might look like this: "Zippoteeth scored

OBJECTIVES FOR THIS LESSON

Discuss solvents and their uses.

Design and conduct an inquiry on stain removal.

Present your results to the rest of the class.

5 on plaque removal but 10 on battery life. Scrubboplaque scored 6 on plaque removal but only 2 on battery life."

Do you think designing the tests that go into making this sort of report is easy? Scientists must take into account many factors and must standardize the tests so they are fair to all the products being tested. Could you design tests like this? In today's lesson, you will have the chance to solve a similar type of problem. This one involves stain removal as well as some topics you investigated in previous lessons—solutions and dissolving.

MATERIALS FOR LESSON 16

For you
1 pair of safety goggles

For your group
3 dropper bottles containing these solvents:
    Water
    Rubbing (iso-propyl) alcohol
    Kerosene
3 plastic cups containing these staining substances:
    Ketchup
    Chocolate syrup
    Vegetable oil
1 black permanent marker
1 ballpoint pen
5 white cotton cloth squares
10 cotton swabs
2 sheets of newspaper
1 sheet of newsprint
    Masking tape

Figure 16.1 *This scientist knows that product testing requires many factors to be taken into account and standardized tests to be used.*

Getting Started

1. Your teacher will ask you to think of examples of liquids that do not contain water. Write your examples in your science notebook. You will be asked to contribute your ideas during a short brainstorming session.

2. After the brainstorming session and discussion, copy the diagram the class has produced into your notebook.

SAFETY TIPS

Wear your safety goggles throughout the inquiry.

Take care not to get solvents or stains on your clothes.

Do not taste any of the substances.

If you spill rubbing alcohol or kerosene, immediately tell your teacher.

Inquiry 16.1
Removing Stains

PROCEDURE

1. One member of your group should collect a plastic box of materials. Check the contents of the box against the materials list.

2. Using the materials in the plastic box, your group should design a test that can be used to compare the effectiveness of the three solvents (in the bottles) at removing five different types of stain. The stains are ketchup, chocolate syrup, vegetable oil, marker pen ink, and ballpoint pen ink. Your teacher may give you some other stains as well. Think about the following questions and test design considerations and discuss them with the rest of your group:

A. How will you standardize your testing procedures so that the results obtained for each solvent and stain can be fairly compared? What elements will you need to standardize?

B. The stains will need to be dry before you test them. How will you accomplish this?

C. How will you score the effectiveness of the stain removers on each stain?

D. How will you present your results so they are easy for others to understand?

E. How will you divide the work among the members of your group?

F. How long will you take to conduct each step of the procedure? (Your teacher will tell you how much total time you have.)

3. In your notebook, write what you are trying to find out. Agree on the materials you are going to use, a procedure, and the design of a scoring rubric (system) and a results table. Record this information in your notebook under the following headings: Materials, Procedure, Scoring Rubric, and Results Table.

4. Draw a large version of your group's results table on the sheet of newsprint.

5. Apply the stains. Write the names of the members of your group on the cloth squares. Allow the stains to dry in the place suggested by your teacher.

6. Continue with your procedure during the next period.

7. Transfer all of your results to the table on the newsprint. Tack or tape the newsprint on the wall nearest your table. Make sure you also make a copy of all the results in your science notebook.

8. Clean up the materials. Dispose of the cotton swabs, cloths, and small containers of staining substances. Return the remaining items to the plastic box.

REFLECTING ON WHAT YOU'VE DONE

1. Discuss the results with members of your group. In your notebook, write any conclusions you can make from your test. Include any comments or suggestions about the effectiveness of your procedure.

2. Your teacher will lead a class discussion. One member of your group will be asked to report on your procedure, scoring rubric, results, and conclusions.

Getting Taken to the Cleaners

Have you ever bought a new piece of clothing, worn it once, put it through the wash, and when you've tried to wear it again, discovered it had shrunk or was completely misshapen? It's only then that you bother to read the label— "Dry clean only."

Dry cleaning is used to clean clothes that would be harmed by water. It is also used to remove stains that are insoluble in water (for example, grease). As the name suggests, dry cleaning involves cleaning without water. (Actually, a very small amount of water is used—you'll find out why later—but not enough to change the name to wet cleaning!) However, even though only a little water is

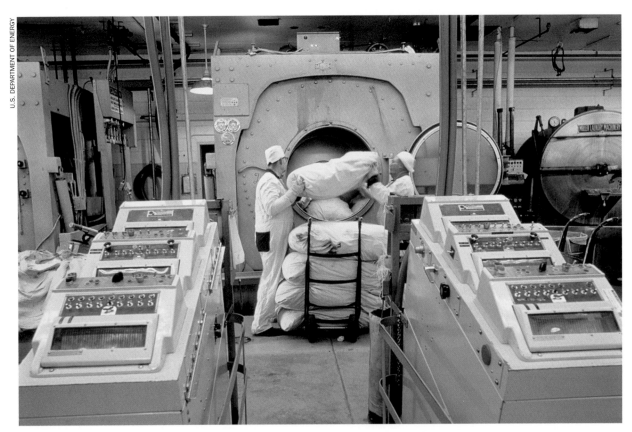

Dry-cleaning machines work somewhat like washing machines, but they use a solvent other than water.

If your dry cleaning smells strongly of solvent, open the windows of your car.

used, the term "dry cleaning" is still a bit deceptive. That's because liquids other than water *are* used.

Early forms of dry cleaning used petroleum solvents such as kerosene. But kerosene is flammable—it burns. After a series of explosions at dry cleaners, the solvent tetrachloroethylene was widely adopted, and it is still used today (along with other solvents). Tetrachloroethylene is not flammable, but its fumes can be toxic in enclosed spaces. That is one reason why, if dry-cleaned clothes smell strongly of solvent, you should drive home from the dry cleaners with your car windows open.

How does dry cleaning work? A dry-cleaning machine is like a giant washing machine. Clothes are placed in the machine. Tetrachloroethylene, mixed with a very small amount of water and a special detergent, is added. (Water is added to remove any stains caused by water-soluble substances.) The tetrachloroethylene flows continuously through the machine until the clothes are clean. Any solvent that remains in the clothes after the cleaning cycle eventually evaporates. All the remaining solvent is recycled. It is

heated until it evaporates and then cooled until it condenses to produce a clean solvent that can be used again.

A new approach to dry cleaning has been developed. This method does not use any toxic dry-cleaning solvents. Special detergents and carbon dioxide, which is the solvent, clean the clothes. The carbon dioxide, a gas normally found in air and very much less toxic to the environment than solvents such as tetrachloroethylene, is put under pressure during the cleaning process. This pressure keeps the carbon dioxide in a liquid state. Both the special detergents and the carbon dioxide can be recycled. Will this more environmentally friendly approach be the future of dry cleaning? ☐

QUESTIONS

1. Why do people who own washing machines still go to the dry cleaners?
2. Can you suggest two advantages of recycling the solvents used in the dry-cleaning process?

MIXING COLORFUL COVERINGS

Why do we use paint and what does it consist of?

Wouldn't the world be a dull place if there were no such thing as paint? Since prehistoric times, paints have been used in art. The earliest cave paintings were made using paints derived from colored soils and rocks or from animals and plants. These were mixed with other substances, such as egg white, which allowed the pigments to spread over and stick to the surface being painted. Today, paints are used to protect and decorate surfaces. They are carefully formulated mixtures, designed to do specific jobs, and are available in a seemingly infinite variety of colors. Let's examine these mixtures more closely and see how the different properties of the substances from which they are made work together.

Most paints consist of pigments, a vehicle, and a solvent, plus other additives

© DAVID MARSLAND

Throughout history, artists have used a wide variety of pigments in their paintings. Many paints contain oxides of metals, which provide color. Bushman rock artists used soils containing reddish brown iron oxide to paint these images. Many modern oil paints contain other metal oxides that produce the vivid colors associated with oil paintings.

CORBIS/PHILADELPHIA MUSEUM OF ART

Van Gogh used bright yellows in many of his paintings (including Still Life: Vase with Twelve Sunflowers, *shown here). A lead chromate pigment provides the yellow color.*

that perform a variety of functions. Pigments give the paint color and also make it opaque (not transparent). The type of pigment used depends on the color of the paint wanted. For example, white paint often contains the pigment titanium dioxide. However, several pigments can be used together in varying quantities to produce a wide range of paint colors. For instance, even though titanium dioxide is used to make white paint, other pigments are often mixed with it to produce paints of

COURTESY OF THE NATIONAL ARCHIVES

This artist is painting a mural. Artists' paints contain many different solvents. Water and turpentine are the most common.

other colors. For example, titanium dioxide is mixed with barium chromate or cadmium sulfide to make yellow paints, with chromium oxide to make green paints, and with ultramarine or dyes such as indanthrone blue to make blue paints. In addition to adding color to paint, titanium dioxide has the ability to hide the surface that is being painted. For this reason it is called a hiding pigment.

Paint must also contain a substance that will make the pigment stick to the surface being painted (like the egg white used by pre-historic cave painters). These bonding substances are called the vehicle. They are usually made from plastic-like substances which, when dry, form a hard, flexible protective coating.

Solvent thins the paint and helps it spread during paint-ing. Mineral spirits are used as solvents in some glossy paints. These dis-solve the vehicle. When the paint dries, a hard film is left behind.

Many emulsion paints and modern latex paints use water as a thinner, although in these cases, the water does not dis-solve the vehicle but keeps it finely divided. When the paint dries, the finely divided emulsion comes together to form a hard, flexible surface.

Paints often contain a variety of additives that perform various functions. They may improve the weather resistance of the paint, affect the way the pigment is dis-persed to produce special finishes, or speed up the drying process. ☐

Paint is a complex mixture designed to be applied as a liquid and to dry into a decorative and hard, but flexible, protective finish.

LESSON 17
Separating Solutes

Is this money genuine? Would you be able to find out by analyzing the ink that was used to print it?

COURTESY OF CAROLINA BIOLOGICAL SUPPLY COMPANY

INTRODUCTION

Most of the mixtures you have examined in this module have consisted of two substances. For example, the solutions you studied were mixtures of a solvent and a solute. In the last lesson, however, you investigated how different solvents could be used to remove more complex mixtures, or stains. The success of stain removal depended on the solubility of the pure substances that made up the stains. Two of the substances you tried to remove were inks. What was the composition of these inks? Were they both made from the same substances? If you made careful observations, you may have some clues to help you answer these questions. You may have noticed some strange things happening to the inks when you added some of the solvents. In this lesson, you will take a closer look at what happens when solvents are added to inks and how some of these properties can be used to identify inks from different sources.

OBJECTIVES FOR THIS LESSON

Use paper chromatography to analyze and identify inks.

Apply paper chromatography techniques to "solve a crime."

Getting Started

1. One member of your group should collect the plastic box.

2. Check the contents of the plastic box against the materials list and remove the apparatus for your pair. (In this lesson, you will work with a partner, but you will share the markers with the other pair in your group.)

3. Put about 25 mL of water into the 250-mL beaker.

4. *Quickly* (for about 1–2 seconds) dip the tip of the green marker into the water.

5. Observe what happens. Answer this question on Student Sheet 17.1: What happened when you put the tip of the green marker into the water?

6. Based on your observations, what do you know about the ink? Write your answer on the student sheet.

7. Your teacher will lead a short discussion about the observations you have made.

MATERIALS FOR
LESSON 17

For you
- 1 copy of Student Sheet 17.1: Analyzing Inks
- 1 copy of Student Sheet 17.2: Comparing Inks
- 1 copy of Student Sheet 17.3: Identifying Inks
- 1 copy of Student Sheet 17: Assessment Review

For you and your lab partner
- 1 250-mL beaker
- 2 pieces of chromatography paper
- 1 pencil
- 1 metric ruler
- Access to water

For your group
- 1 brown marker
- 1 green marker
- 1 red marker
- 3 black markers (labeled B, C, and D)

CHANGING MELTING AND BOILING POINTS

Do you know what is inside the strange building shown in this photograph? The building is used to store salt that is spread on the road when weather conditions are below the freezing point of water. What effect will the salt have on icy roads? Why store the salt in a building?

This truck removes snow and spreads salt. How does spreading salt on roads reduce accidents?

A solution of antifreeze is used to fill car radiators. It lowers the freezing point of the water in the radiator of the car. It also raises its boiling point and reduces corrosion. Why are the properties of this solution useful to motorists? Why isn't salt used instead?

Inquiry 18.3
Investigating Solid Solutions

PROCEDURE

1. In this inquiry, you will investigate how impurities affect the melting point of three metal mixtures called solders. Because these solders melt at temperatures above the range of the thermometers you will use, you will measure the amount of time it takes for each of the solders to melt. You will then compare these measurements to determine the melting points of the solders. Your teacher will demonstrate how the apparatus in this inquiry should be used. Watch carefully and then read the instructions and Safety Tips before you start.

2. Assemble the apparatus as shown in Figure 18.1, but *do not place the burner into position under the stand until Step 6.*

Figure 18.1 *How to assemble the alcohol burner apparatus for Inquiry 18.2. (Your burner may differ from this one.) Do not place the burner into position under the stand until Step 6.*

3. Place the pieces of solder on the aluminum pan in the same positions as those shown in Figure 18.2.

4. Make sure the aluminum pan is positioned in the center of the gauze. Make sure you know where each color-coded piece of solder is by completing the diagram in Step 1 on Student Sheet 18.3. **Warning:** As the solder gets hot, the color codes may disappear.

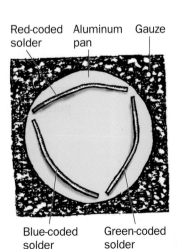

Red-coded solder   Aluminum pan   Gauze

Blue-coded solder   Green-coded solder

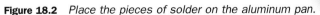

Figure 18.2 *Place the pieces of solder on the aluminum pan.*

The Samurai's Sword

The properties of metal objects are determined not only by all the different metals that make them up but also by the way the metals are mixed together and treated. For thousands of years, metal workers, or smiths, have been altering the properties of metals by heating, hammering, and using other treatments to make objects as diverse as springs and gun barrels. The famous swords of the Samurai warriors of medieval Japan are one example of how smiths used the properties of particular metals for specific purposes.

The first Samurai were soldiers who were hired by landowners to protect their property from bands of robbers. From the 12th to the 19th century, even though Japan had emperors, the Samurai actually ruled Japan. The sons of Samurai were trained from early childhood for careers

The Samurai's sword was a formidable weapon.

as warriors. A young man began his career at about age 15, when he received his first sword in a special ceremony.

Although each Samurai also carried a bow and arrow (and was trained in wrestling and judo), sword fighting was his most important skill. And the Samurai's

swords were special indeed. Each Samurai had a long sword and a short one. The long sword, called the *katana*, was his main weapon. Its steel blade was designed to kill an enemy with one swipe!

To make a *katana*, a swordsmith used two types of steel.

The core of the sword was made of soft, flexible, low-carbon steel (an alloy of iron with a little carbon). The jacket, or outer part of the sword, was made of hard steel that contained a greater proportion of carbon than did the core. The combination of these two kinds of steel gave the sword the flexibility to withstand a hard blow and a hard, razor sharp edge that would not be dulled during battle.

The swordsmith treated both steels with different techniques that improved the performance of the sword even further. He began by heating a lump of raw low-carbon steel—about the size of a brick—in a forge (a furnace that burns charcoal at very high temperatures). The swordsmith then hammered the steel on an anvil until it was flat. Then he folded it in half crosswise and

Expert modern swordsmith Akitsugu Amada is one of two swordsmiths in Japan with the title Ningen Kokuho (Living National Treasure).

hammered it out again. He repeated this process many times to drive out any impurities from the metal. Finally, he shaped it into a long, thin wedge.

Next, the swordsmith began to work on the high-carbon steel. He followed the same process as the one he used for the low-carbon steel, but this time, he hammered and folded many more times. The final piece of metal had up to 30,000 folds or layers. The swordsmith made the jacket somewhat longer than the core.

Next, he joined together the two parts of the blade. The jacket was wrapped around the core, and the swordsmith heated and hammered the two pieces until they formed a solid bond. He had to be extremely careful; if an air bubble or piece of dirt remained between the two parts of the blade, the sword would be worthless in battle.

The blade was then tempered, a process that is used to control the properties of the steel. The blade was heated and then cooled by being plunged into water. The swordsmith coated the sword with clay to control the cooling process. Where the coat of clay was thick, the steel would cool more slowly, and this would make it flexible. The edge of the blade was given a thin coat of clay, which allowed it to cool very quickly, a process that made the edge even harder.

The swordsmith sharpened and polished the blade. The layers, or grain, were visible on the shiny surface. Finally, he tested the blade—on iron sheets, armor, and, sometimes, the bodies of executed criminals.

The Samurai swords were deadly but beautiful. The blades were decorated, and the handles were inlaid with pearls and other jewels.

Samurai swords were passed from generation to generation. Upon reaching manhood, a son received his father's sword, along with stories of the brave acts that had been accomplished with it. ☐

Kenji Mishina, a great master sword polisher, carefully polishes a Samurai sword.

QUESTION

What techniques did the swordsmith use to modify the properties of different parts of a *katana* blade? Investigate how these techniques are applied for different purposes today.

Ice Cream in the Old Days

Which came first, ice cream or freezers? Everyone knows that a freezer is needed to store ice cream. To keep ice cream solid, it has to be stored well below the freezing point of water (0 °C). Making ice cream also requires the same low temperatures. People didn't have freezers in the old days, so were they able to make ice cream?

The answer is yes. Most people used to make their own ice cream at home. They would have ice delivered to their house by an ice-making company, or they would use ice they had collected in winter and stored underground. They would start by making an ice cream mixture. They would combine the mixture in a metal container (one that's good at conducting heat) and then place the container in a bucket containing crushed ice and a little water.

Next, they added salt to the ice. The ice

Delicious! But how was ice cream made without a freezer?

This ice cream machine required the use of ice and salt to lower the temperature of the ice cream mixture to the point where it would freeze.

would immediately start to melt. To melt, ice takes in heat from its surroundings, cooling down the container of the ice cream mixture to below the freezing point of water. They would continually stir the ice cream mixture so it produced small ice crystals, which gives ice cream its creamy texture. Sometimes they would have to use as much as a pound of salt to make the ice cream.

You can make your own ice cream by following Great Grandma's vanilla ice cream recipe. After you make it, you can add your favorite toppings. ◻

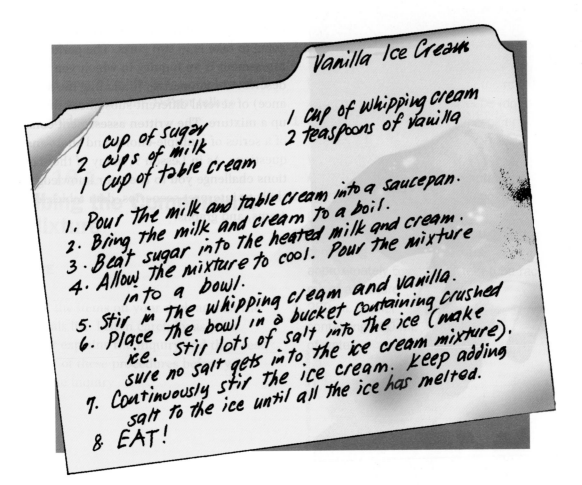

Vanilla Ice Cream

1 cup of sugar
2 cups of milk
1 cup of table cream
1 cup of whipping cream
2 teaspoons of vanilla

1. Pour the milk and table cream into a saucepan.
2. Bring the milk and cream to a boil.
3. Beat sugar into the heated milk and cream.
4. Allow the mixture to cool. Pour the mixture into a bowl.
5. Stir in the whipping cream and vanilla.
6. Place the bowl in a bucket containing crushed ice. Stir lots of salt into the ice (make sure no salt gets into the ice cream mixture).
7. Continuously stir the ice cream. Keep adding salt to the ice until all the ice has melted.
8. EAT!

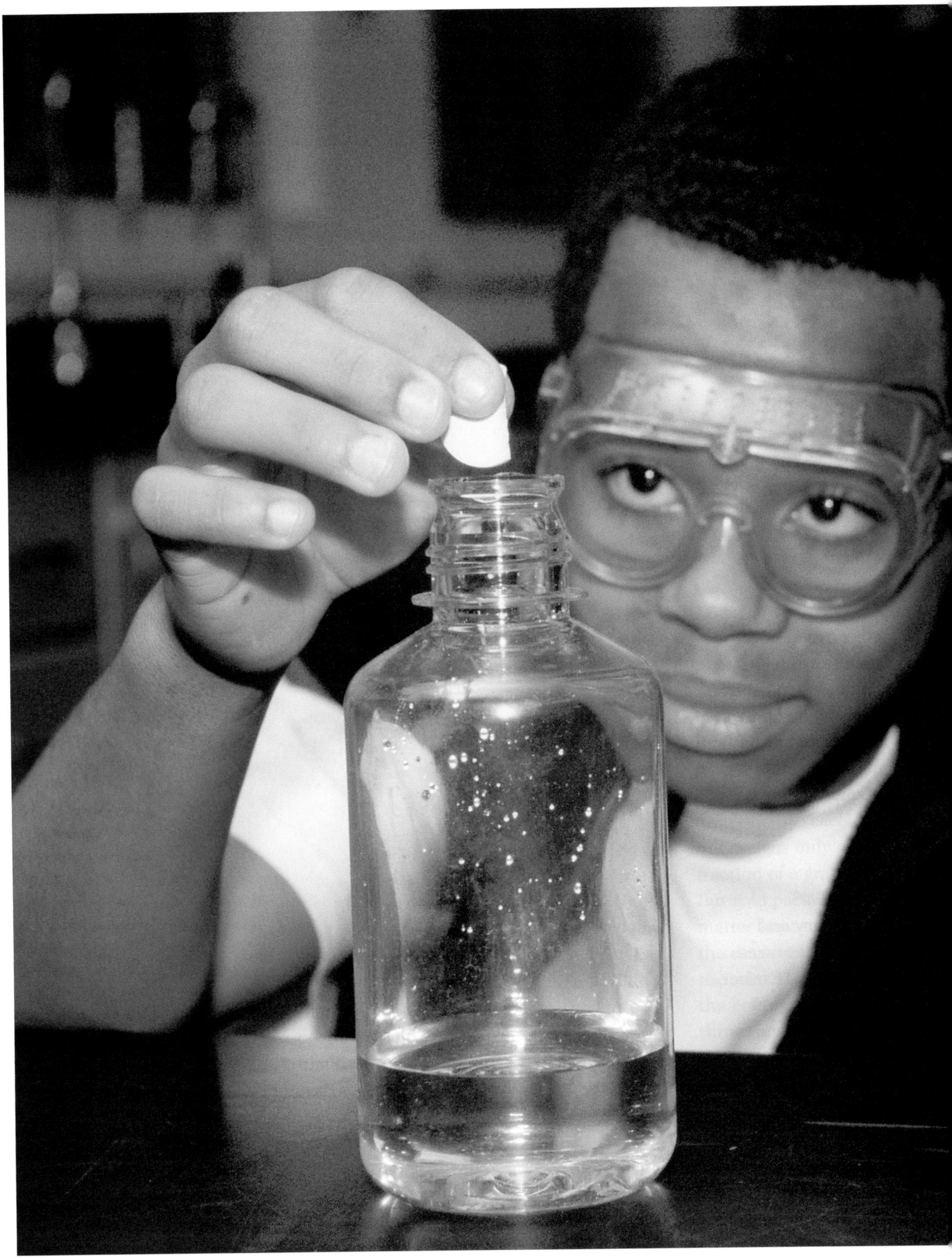

© TERRY G. McCREA/SMITHSONIAN INSTITUTION

PART **3** Compounds, Elements, and Chemical Reactions

Breaking Down a Compound

The surface of the Earth is four-fifths water.
What is water made from?

NASA

INTRODUCTION

In the first part of this module, you looked at the characteristic properties of pure substances. In the second part, you investigated how these properties can differ from the properties of mixtures. In this part, you will focus on two groups of pure substances known as elements and compounds. In this lesson, you will examine the composition of the pure substance you have encountered most often during the course of this module—water. You know that water has several characteristic properties that can identify it as a single substance rather than a mixture. These properties include its appearance, density, melting and boiling points, and ability to dissolve a wide range of solutes. You will investigate what happens to water when electricity is passed through it. Sometimes, passing electricity through a liquid can give clues about the composition of the liquid. If water is a pure substance, why try to find out its composition? Do the inquiry and find out what happens!

OBJECTIVES FOR THIS LESSON

Conduct an experiment to determine what happens when electricity is passed through water.

Investigate some physical and chemical properties of gases.

Discuss the differences between compounds and elements.

Getting Started

1. Have you ever heard the terms "element" and "compound"? What do these terms mean? Without referring to a dictionary or your Student Guide, write definitions for each of these terms in your science notebook.

2. In your notebook, give two examples of an element and two examples of a compound.

3. Your teacher will lead a brainstorming session on what you think these words mean. You will look at these ideas again at the end of the lesson.

SAFETY TIPS

Wear safety goggles throughout this inquiry.

Tie back long hair.

MATERIALS FOR LESSON 20

For you
- 1 copy of Student Sheet 20.1: Electrolysis of Water
- 1 pair of safety goggles

For your group
- 1 plastic container
- 2 test tubes
- 1 electrode stand
- 1 jar of sodium sulfate
- 1 lab scoop
- 1 plastic spoon
- 1 wooden splint
- 2 6-V batteries (shared with another group)
- 1 insulated connector wire with alligator clips
- Access to water
- Access to a burner

Inquiry 20.1
Splitting Water

PROCEDURE

1. Your teacher will demonstrate the procedure for passing an electric current through water. After the demonstration, follow Steps 2 through 10 to set up your apparatus.

2. Place the electrode stand in the plastic container.

3. Make sure the leads hang over the side of the container.

4. Add water to the container so that the tips of the electrodes are covered by about 1 cm of water (see Figure 20.1).

5. Add two lab scoops of sodium sulfate to the water.

6. Stir the solution with the plastic spoon.

7. Submerge one of the test tubes in the container of sodium sulfate solution (see Figure 20.2).

Figure 20.1 *Place the electrode stand in the plastic container and add water.*

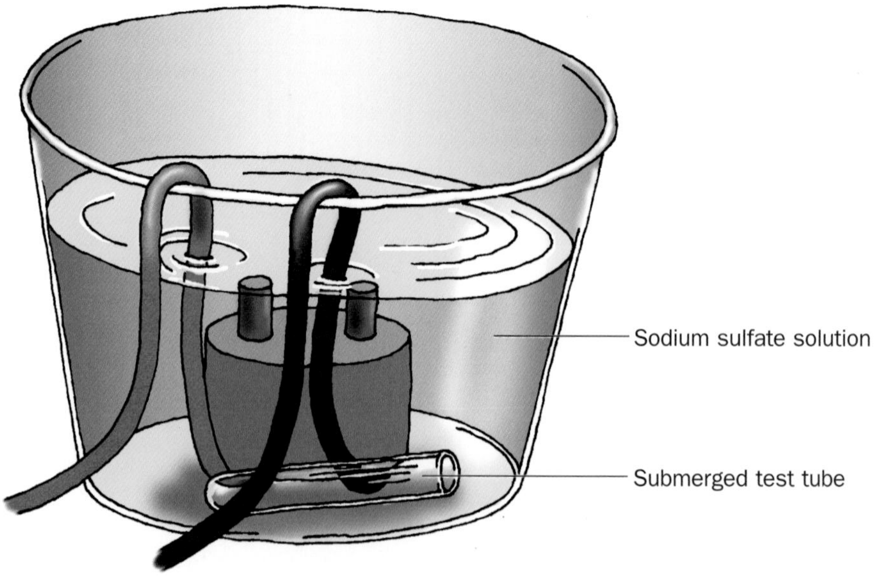

Water

Figure 20.2 *Submerge the tube and make sure it is full of sodium sulfate solution.*

Sodium sulfate solution

Submerged test tube

8. When the tube is full of solution, place your thumb or finger over its top. Making sure the open end of the tube is below the liquid, place the opening of the tube over one of the electrodes. The tube must still be full of liquid.

9. Repeat Steps 7 and 8 with the second test tube. (Do not worry if a few small bubbles of air get into the tubes.) Figure 20.3 shows what your apparatus should look like. Wash your hands after handling the tubes.

10. Clip the connector wires onto the batteries. Clip the red connector wire to the positive terminal of one battery and the black connector wire to the negative terminal of the other battery. Make sure the two remaining terminals on the batteries are connected. (See Figure 20.4.) You will be sharing the two batteries with another group. Figure 20.5 shows how to set up the apparatus for both groups.

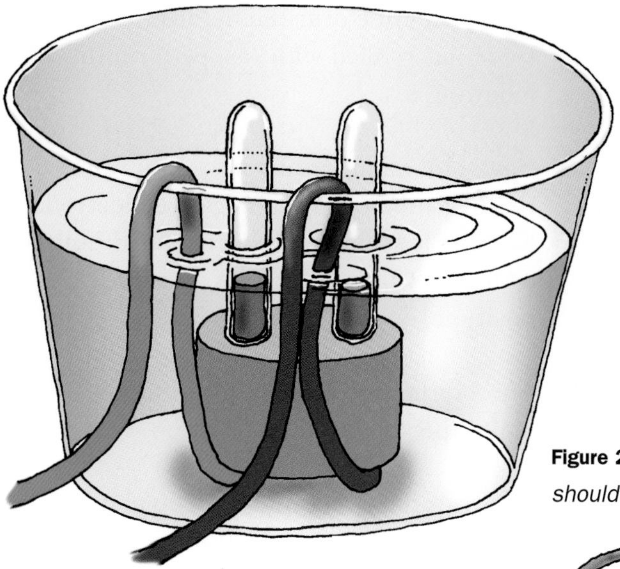

Figure 20.3 *At this stage, your apparatus should look like this.*

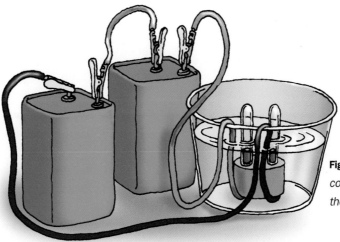

Figure 20.4 *Clip the connector wires onto the batteries as shown.*

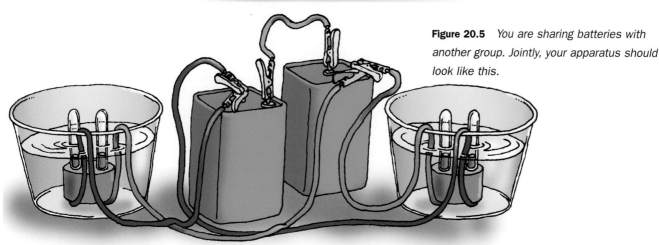

Figure 20.5 *You are sharing batteries with another group. Jointly, your apparatus should look like this.*

11. If you have assembled your apparatus correctly, you should soon start to see something happening near the electrodes. What do you observe happening at each of the electrodes? Write your answers on the student sheet.

12. What do you observe about the volumes of the two substances collected in the tubes? Write your answer on the student sheet.

13. Your teacher will conduct a class discussion about your observations. Be prepared to participate.

14. You *(or your teacher, if you do not have time to collect enough of each gas)* can test the gases produced in each test tube by putting a burning splint into each tube. If your group is conducting this test, follow these instructions:

   A. Disconnect the battery from your apparatus.

   B. Have one member of your group ignite the splint so it is burning.

   C. Have another group member carefully remove a gas-filled tube from the negative electrode. It is alright if a little solution in the tube empties back into the plastic container. Hold the tube with the open end down (inverted.)

   D. With the open end down, tilt the test tube at a 45° angle and quickly put the lit end of the splint into the mouth of the test tube. Look *and listen!*

   E. Record your results under "Tube 1" in Table 1 on Student Sheet 20.1.

   F. Refill the test tube with sodium sulfate solution, reconnect the battery, and continue to collect gas.

   G. When the test tube over the positive electrode is filled with gas, perform the same test.

   H. Record the results under "Tube 2" in Table 1.

15. When the tube over the negative electrode has refilled with gas, perform the following test:

   A. Have one member of your group remove the test tube from the negative electrode, keeping it sealed with his or her thumb or finger. Hold the tube in an upright position (open end up.)

   B. Another member of the group should ignite the splint.

   C. Blow out the splint and then quickly put the glowing end into the tube of gas.

   D. Carefully observe what happens and record the results under "Tube 3" in Table 1.

   E. Repeat the test with a tube full of gas from the positive electrode.

   F. Record your results under "Tube 4" in Table 1.

16. Hydrogen gas burns with a squeaky pop, and oxygen relights a glowing splint (or makes it glow much brighter). Based on your experimental evidence, what is inside each tube? Write your answers under Steps 4a and b on the student sheet.

17. Read "The Electrolysis of Water," on page 175.

THE ELECTROLYSIS OF WATER

In Inquiry 20.1, electricity was used to split water into hydrogen and oxygen. This process is called electrolysis ("electro" refers to electricity and "lysis" means "to break apart"). To break down water through the process of electrolysis, electricity must be able to flow through the water and complete an electrical circuit.

Electricity does not flow easily through pure water because pure water is a poor conductor of electricity, making it difficult to complete an electrical circuit. Adding sodium sulfate to pure water helps the water conduct electricity, which makes it easier to complete an electrical circuit. The energy from the electric current causes a chemical reaction to take place. During the reaction, sodium sulfate does not produce any products that can be detected. All of the gases produced during the electrolysis of water come from the water.

REFLECTING ON WHAT YOU'VE DONE

1. Write the answers to the following questions on Student Sheet 20.1:

A. Which two gases make up water?

B. You know that water is a pure substance. You have found out that it is made from two gases. Both gases are also pure substances. However, these gases cannot be broken down into other substances. Pure substances that cannot be broken down into other substances are called elements. Pure substances that are made up from more than one element are called compounds. Do you think water is an element or a compound?

C. Unlike mixtures, pure substances that are compounds always have the same ratio of elements in them; in other words, they have fixed compositions or formulas. What is the ratio of hydrogen to oxygen in water?

D. Water is sometimes written as a formula, H_2O. What do you think this formula means?

2. Think about how the characteristic properties of water differ from the characteristic properties of hydrogen and oxygen. Read about some of them in the reader "Hydrogen and Oxygen," on pages 176–177. Your teacher will collect your ideas and compile them in a table. Copy this table in your notebook.

3. Review the definitions of the terms "element" and "compound" that you wrote at the beginning of the lesson. Discuss with your partner how your ideas have changed. Write your ideas in your notebook.

HYDROGEN AND OXYGEN

Water is a compound made up of two elements—hydrogen and oxygen. The characteristic properties of these elements are different from those of water. However, hydrogen and oxygen have some common properties. They are both colorless, odorless gases, and they both readily react with other elements—making them "reactive" elements. But in many ways they are very different from each other.

Hydrogen has the lowest density of all the elements. It is very reactive, which is one reason why it is present in only very small quantities in air. It reacts with oxygen. You reacted it with oxygen when it burned with a squeaky pop. What do you think was made in that chemical reaction?

It may come as a surprise to you to discover that hydrogen is the most common element in the universe. The sun and other stars are mainly hydrogen gas. Hydrogen is found in many compounds. For example, all acids contain hydrogen.

Oxygen reacts with other substances. Some of the properties of oxygen were discussed in the reader "Air Heads" (in Lesson 4). Oxygen is needed for burning to take place. Things burn well in oxygen, producing hotter flames. For example, what happened to the glowing splint when it was put into a tube of

Water is a compound formed when inflammable hydrogen reacts with oxygen. Here, it is being used to put out a fire. Like all compounds, the properties of water are very different from those of the elements from which it is composed.

© PETER SKINNER/PHOTO RESEARCHERS, INC.

almost pure oxygen? Some welding and metal-cutting equipment use flammable gases and pure oxygen to produce the high temperatures needed to melt metal.

Oxygen also reacts slowly with many substances. Many compounds containing oxygen are called oxides. You've already come across the two oxides that are gases—carbon dioxide and sulfur dioxide—but most oxides are solids. In fact, oxygen is the most common element in the Earth's crust, but most of it is combined with other elements to form minerals that make up rocks.

When flammable gases such as acetylene are burned in pure oxygen, very high temperatures are produced. This oxyacetylene torch burns a mixture of acetylene gas and oxygen, which produces a flame hot enough to cut or weld steel.

The Properties of Hydrogen and the Death of an Airship

Date: Thursday
May 6, 1937
Time: 7:25 p.m.
Location: Lakehurst
Air Station
New Jersey

As the 804-foot-long, hydrogen-filled airship, the *Hindenburg*, passed over Lakehurst Air Station, it turned to make its final approach. The crew opened ballast tanks to slow its descent, and water gushed from the bottom of the ship, soaking the mooring party below. Everyone at the station was watching the *Hindenburg* as this masterpiece of modern technology hovered 200 feet above the ground. Near the giant airship, some members of the press adjusted their cameras and sound recorders while others scribbled in their notebooks. In the parking lot, more photographers stood on the tops of cars, attempting to get a better view.

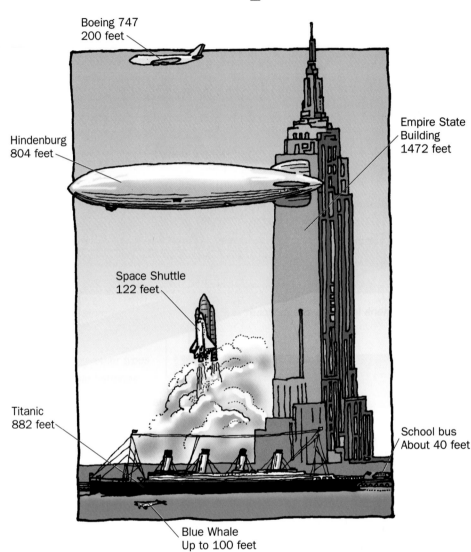

Boeing 747
200 feet

Hindenburg
804 feet

Empire State
Building
1472 feet

Space Shuttle
122 feet

Titanic
882 feet

School bus
About 40 feet

Blue Whale
Up to 100 feet

The Hindenburg *was bigger than a jumbo jet and almost as long as the* Titanic.

Inside the cabin of the *Hindenburg*, some of the passengers were looking down at the crowds below, searching for the faces of family and friends. They could see the landing crew preparing to catch the ropes dropped from the airship. Suddenly, a deep thump emanated from the stern of the airship. People on the ground began to scream, and the men waiting below the airship began to run. The sky lit up.

Inside the airship, all was chaos. In the officers' mess hall, Werner Franz, a 14-year-old cabin boy,

The hydrogen-filled airship, Hindenburg, *flies over New York City. Why was hydrogen used to fill this airship?*

was clearing away plates. As he reached into a cupboard, he felt the whole ship jerk. Plates from the cupboard fell on top of him. He managed to get up and stumble out into the gangway. Everything seemed to be on fire. A huge wall of flames was coming straight at him.

What Werner didn't know was that during docking, the fabric surrounding the hydrogen envelope that kept the ship aloft had somehow ignited. Not only did

the fabric burn like dry paper, it started an explosive chemical reaction between the hydrogen inside the envelope and the oxygen in the air. The German engineers who had designed the *Hindenburg* had chosen the wrong materials to make an airship. They had built a floating bomb!

Frantically, Werner scrambled away from the flames, toward the front of the airship. The ship lurched again, tilting backward toward the stern. Werner fell

and began to slide into the fire. Gathering all his strength, he desperately began to crawl along the floor away

from the fire. He could feel the heat through the soles of his shoes. The flames were licking at his legs.

Just before docking, the Hindenburg *burst into flames.*

The fire consumed the entire airship. What substance was formed in this chemical reaction?

The Hindenburg's surviving officers and crew, including Werner Franz, who is standing in the middle at the front, found out firsthand about the dangers of some chemical reactions.

Suddenly, a gush of water knocked Werner flat against the floor. One of the ship's water tanks had burst above him, temporarily extinguishing the nearby fire. But a few seconds later, the fire was back. Werner grabbed at a nearby hatch, kicked it open, and jumped. Winded, he lay on the ground. Screams were still coming from all around. Pulling himself to his feet, he began to run away from the flames. He saw the Hindenburg's captain running in the opposite direction, back to the ship. He was trying to save some of the passengers. Werner turned to run back to help him. As he did so, he was grabbed from behind by an American naval officer, who pulled him to safety.

Thirty-five passengers and crew and one person on the ground died in the flames and wreckage of the Hindenburg, as did the dreams of its designers and travel by airship. All of this happened because two elements (which form water!) reacted together to create a disaster. □

Extracting Aluminum

This aluminum and gold baby rattle was made for Prince Louis Napoleon of France in 1856. At that time, aluminum, like gold, was considered a rare and valuable metal.

Precious Metal

No one knew about aluminum until 1825. That's when a Danish chemist first extracted pinhead-sized bits of aluminum from a mineral called alumina. But, extracting aluminum from alumina was very difficult, and for most of the 1800s, aluminum was rare and expensive. It was so valuable that kings and queens had fine tea sets and ornamental objects made of aluminum.

Common Metal

Even though aluminum was once considered very rare, it is the most common metal in

In 1884, aluminum was even chosen for a place of honor at the very tip of the Washington Monument, because it was such a rare metal.

Aluminum is an excellent material for use in lightweight sports equipment, such as this baseball bat. What other sports equipment is made from aluminum?

Earth's crust, making up 8 percent of Earth's crust. This aluminum is not found as pure aluminum metal but is combined with other elements in the form of aluminum compounds. Today, aluminum is used for everything from airplane frames to soda cans and baseball bats. It is shiny, strong, and lightweight. It doesn't rust and can be shaped and cast. It's even inexpensive enough to use for wrapping leftovers. But aluminum did not become economical until a young inventor working in his backyard lab came up with a low-cost way to extract it from alumina.

Early Start

An eager experimenter, Charles Martin Hall began work on aluminum in 1880. Just 20 years old, he was in his first year at Oberlin College in Ohio.

Backyard Inventor

Working in a woodshed behind his house, Hall set out to find a way to use electric current to get aluminum metal out of alumina, which contains aluminum and oxygen. The hard part was finding the right liquid in which

Charles Martin Hall developed a commercial process for producing aluminum.

to dissolve the mineral. Water wouldn't work. Passing electricity through a water solution of alumina only caused the water to break down into hydrogen and oxygen gas. Instead, Hall dissolved it in another mineral, called cryolite. This was tricky. First he had to melt the cryolite by heating it to more than 1000 °C. He used carbon electrodes to carry the current, because metal electrodes would have melted.

Success!

On February 23, 1886, Hall had his first success. After running current through his setup for a few hours, he found several small globs of aluminum inside. He went on to start Alcoa Corporation, still one of the world's largest producers of aluminum. When Hall died in 1914, much of his fortune went to schools around the world. Oberlin College honors his generosity with this aluminum statue. ◻

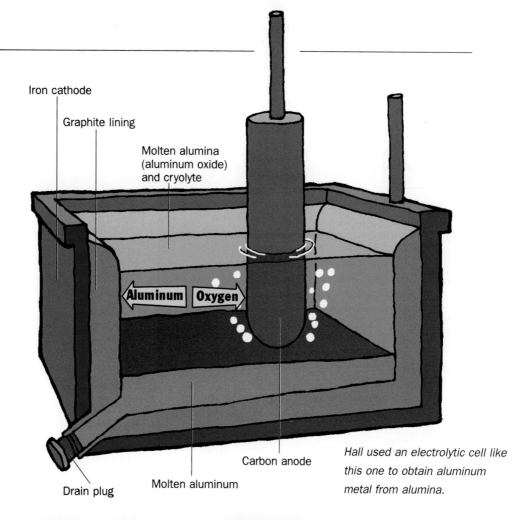

Iron cathode

Graphite lining

Molten alumina (aluminum oxide) and cryolyte

Aluminum ← → Oxygen

Carbon anode

Drain plug

Molten aluminum

Hall used an electrolytic cell like this one to obtain aluminum metal from alumina.

© ALCOA, INC.

The man and his metal: This statue of Charles Martin Hall is made from aluminum.

© ALCOA, INC.

Hall's original samples of aluminum rest on top of his notes about the process he invented.

21
Examining and Grouping Elements

Marie Curie, working with her husband Pierre, discovered two elements in 1898 while investigating the radioactive element uranium. They named the first element polonium after her home country, Poland. They named the second one radium because it was very radioactive. In 1903, Marie was awarded the Nobel Prize for her work. She was also awarded a Nobel Prize in 1911 for her work on radioactive elements. Marie Curie was the first person to receive two Nobel Prizes.

© GRAZIA NERI/WOODFIN CAMP & ASSOCIATES

INTRODUCTION

More than 100 different elements exist. They make up all matter. How many elements have you seen or could you recognize? In the last lesson, you obtained two elements, hydrogen and oxygen, by splitting water, a compound. You have come across some others in this module. Sulfur and iron are two. You probably know what some other elements look like, such as gold, silver, and aluminum. But what about silicon, the second most common element in Earth's crust? (Oxygen is the most common.) Or what about calcium, which is found combined with other elements as a compound in bones and teeth? Did you know that each time you take a breath you inhale the elements argon and neon? What are their characteristic properties?

Do not be surprised if you do not recognize many elements in your daily life. Identifying the elements took scientists hundreds of years. Most elements have been recognized only during the past 200 years. The reason chemists had to work so hard to identify all the elements known today is that most elements are reactive. That

OBJECTIVES FOR THIS LESSON

Describe the appearance of several elements.

Perform tests and make observations to determine some physical properties of elements.

Collect information on elements and organize it into a table.

Use the information collected to classify elements into groups.

Compare your classification system with one used by chemists.

is, they tend to combine with other elements to form compounds. Therefore, they usually exist in chemical compounds rather than by themselves. Water, for example, is produced when hydrogen combines with oxygen in a chemical reaction. You observed that reaction in Lesson 20 when you heard hydrogen burn with a squeaky pop, although you probably did not notice that water vapor was being produced!

When you have a large collection of different items, it is often useful to put them into groups. Think of your kitchen at home. You probably have a drawer that contains silverware (probably divided into knives, forks, and spoons). You may also have several cupboards: one for pans, one for plates, and one for glasses. These items are often classified according to their use and sometimes according to their appearance.

After scientists discovered many elements, they began to classify them according to their characteristic properties. By placing elements in groups, scientists could predict how they would behave or react with other elements, what their physical properties would be, and how they could be used. Scientists could even use this classification system to predict the existence of other elements that had not yet been discovered. In this lesson, you will try your hand at classifying some elements.

MATERIALS FOR LESSON 21

For you
1 copy of Student Sheet 21.1a: Examining and Grouping Elements
1 copy of Student Sheet 21.1b: The Periodic Table

For your group
1 black marker
1 sheet of newsprint
Masking tape

Getting Started

1. Your teacher will refer to Lesson 20 while reviewing the terms "element" and "compound."

2. Participate in a brainstorming session on elements and their characteristic properties.

3. Your teacher will construct a list of your ideas about elements and their characteristic properties. At the end of the lesson, you will look at this list again to discover how much you have learned about elements.

Inquiry 21.1
Investigating and Classifying Elements

PROCEDURE

1. Look carefully at Table 1 on Student Sheet 21.1a. You are going to use this table to collect data on 25 different elements. Your teacher will demonstrate how to collect information and will help you complete the table for the elements shown in Figures 21.1 and 21.2. (Use Figure 21.3 when your teacher instructs you to do so.)

Zinc

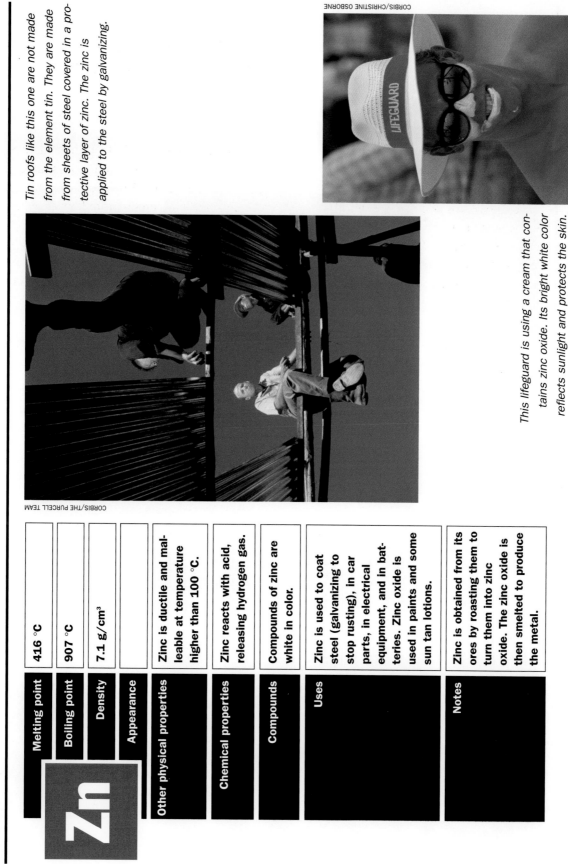

Zn

Melting point	416 °C
Boiling point	907 °C
Density	7.1 g/cm³
Appearance	
Other physical properties	Zinc is ductile and malleable at temperature higher than 100 °C.
Chemical properties	Zinc reacts with acid, releasing hydrogen gas.
Compounds	Compounds of zinc are white in color.
Uses	Zinc is used to coat steel (galvanizing) to stop rusting), in car parts, in electrical equipment, and in batteries. Zinc oxide is used in paints and some sun tan lotions.
Notes	Zinc is obtained from its ores by roasting them to turn them into zinc oxide. The zinc oxide is then smelted to produce the metal.

CORBIS/THE PURCELL TEAM

Tin roofs like this one are not made from the element tin. They are made from sheets of steel covered in a protective layer of zinc. The zinc is applied to the steel by galvanizing.

CORBIS/CHRISTINE OSBORNE

This lifeguard is using a cream that contains zinc oxide. Its bright white color reflects sunlight and protects the skin.

Figure 21.1 *Use the facts and photos shown here and the tests demonstrated by your teacher to complete the information for zinc in Table 1 on Student Sheet 21.1a.*

Uranium

Melting point	1132 °C
Boiling point	3818 °C
Density	19.1 g/cm³
Appearance	
Other physical properties	Uranium is radioactive and malleable, but it is not a very good conductor of electricity.
Chemical properties	Uranium gets a thin coat of oxide when left in the air, and it reacts with water. Uranium powder or chips react violently with air.
Compounds	Uranium compounds come in a variety of colors (uranium dioxide, dark brown; uranium trioxide, orange; uranium fluoride, white).
Uses	Uranium is used in nuclear weapons and nuclear reactors.
Notes	Uranium is highly radioactive, and even small amounts can be a health hazard.

U.S. DEPT. OF ENERGY/PHOTO RESEARCHERS, INC.

Uranium is used inside nuclear reactors and nuclear weapons.

COURTESY OF THE NATIONAL ARCHIVES

A nuclear bomb containing uranium was dropped by the United States on Hiroshima, Japan, toward the end of World War II. Because of their terrifying destructiveness, only two nuclear bombs have ever been used in war. The other, dropped on the Japanese city of Nagasaki, contained a different radioactive metal, called plutonium.

Figure 21.2 Use the facts and photos shown here to help you complete the information for uranium in Table 1 on Student Sheet 21.1a.

Helium

He		
Melting point	−272 °C	
Boiling point	−269 °C	
Density	0.00018 g/cm³	
Appearance	Helium is colorless.	
Other physical properties	Helium is the second least dense element.	
Chemical properties	Helium is odorless and does not react easily with other elements.	
Compounds		
Uses	Helium is used to inflate weather and party balloons as well as modern airships and blimps. It is mixed with oxygen for use by divers.	
Notes	Helium is the second most abundant gas in the universe. It was discovered in the sun by a technique known as spectroscopy before it was found on Earth. It gets its name from Helios, the god of the sun in Greek mythology.	

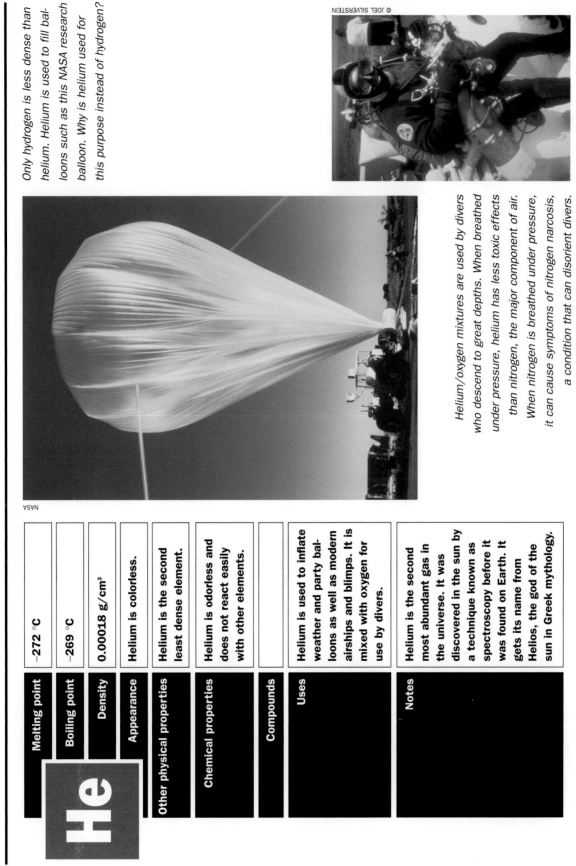

NASA

© JOEL SILVERSTEIN

Only hydrogen is less dense than helium. Helium is used to fill balloons such as this NASA research balloon. Why is helium used for this purpose instead of hydrogen?

Helium/oxygen mixtures are used by divers who descend to great depths. When breathed under pressure, helium has less toxic effects than nitrogen, the major component of air. When nitrogen is breathed under pressure, it can cause symptoms of nitrogen narcosis, a condition that can disorient divers.

Figure 21.3 *When instructed by your teacher, use the facts and photos shown here to enter the information for helium in Table 1 on Student Sheet 21.1a.*

2. Using your observations from Lesson 20 and your own knowledge, complete the rows in Table 1 for hydrogen and oxygen.

3. Participate in a class discussion of your information on hydrogen and oxygen in Table 1. If additional information about these elements arises during the discussion, add it to your table.

4. Your teacher will explain how you should investigate some other elements. Follow along as your teacher reviews Steps 5 through 9 of this procedure.

5. The elements are arranged in stations around the room. For each element, there is a card that looks similar to Figure 21.1, 21.2, or 21.3. Some of these cards have missing information. You will need to examine and test the elements to determine what some of their properties are.

6. For some elements, you must determine whether they conduct electricity (allow electricity to pass through them) or whether they are insulators (do not allow electricity to pass through them). See Figure 21.4 for information on how to perform this test.

7. If a paper clip is at the station, you should investigate the hardness of the element (see Figure 21.5). First, try scratching the element with your fingernail. If this has no effect, try using the end of the paper clip. Is the element hard or soft compared with your fingernail and the paper clip? What does the scratched surface of the element look like?

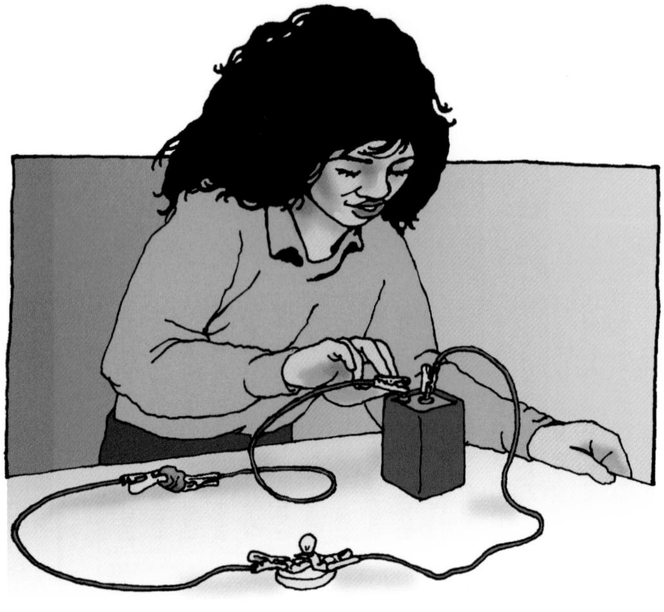

Figure 21.4 *For some elements, you will perform a test to determine whether they conduct electricity. Make a conductivity-testing apparatus. Test the element as shown. If the bulb lights, the element conducts electricity. The brighter the bulb, the better the element conducts electricity.*

Figure 21.5 *Use your fingernail and the paper clip to determine how hard the element is. Also observe how the surface of the element looks after it has been scratched.*

8. Use the magnet to determine whether an element is magnetic.

9. You and your partner will be assigned to a numbered station. Go to that station and start collecting the information you need to complete Table 1. Do not transfer all of the information on the card to the table. Select only the information that you think you need. (Remember that the photographs and their captions contain useful information.) You have 5 minutes to investigate each element.

10. When your teacher calls time, leave the card, element, and any apparatus where you found it. Move to the next station. (If you are at station 20, move to station 1.)

11. When you have collected information on all of the elements at the stations, return to your place. Your teacher will outline how you should place your elements in groups and will ask for your ideas on grouping the elements.

12. Working with the other pair in your group, try to identify at least five groups of elements. Place the elements in these groups. Remember that most elements will fit into more than one group.

13. Write your ideas in your science notebook. When you think you have useful groups of elements, transfer the information from your notebook to the newsprint (see Figure 21.6). When you have finished writing all five groups, attach the sheet of newsprint to the wall.

Figure 21.6 *Record your groups of elements on the newsprint. Make sure the lettering is easily read from the other side of your classroom.*

REFLECTING ON WHAT YOU'VE DONE

1. Participate in a class discussion about how you decided on groupings of elements.

2. Your teacher will compare your classification with an existing one called the periodic table. This table uses the symbols you copied from the Element Cards. Mark where some of the different groups are on your copy of the periodic table (Student Sheet 21.1b). You will notice there are many more elements than the ones you investigated in the inquiry. Some of them fall under the groups you chose.

3. Refer to the list of elements and characteristic properties compiled by the class at the start of the lesson. Discuss the following questions with other members of your group:

   A. *How correct were the original examples and characteristic properties of elements you suggested in "Getting Started"?*

   B. *What changes would you now make to this list?*

Dmitry's Card Game

It's interesting how different skills can be brought together to contribute to scientific discovery. Consider the story of Dmitry Mendeleyev and his card game that changed the face of chemistry.

Mendeleyev was a Russian college professor who loved to play cards. He was also looking for a way to organize the elements. To accomplish this, he wrote the symbols, characteristic properties, and other information for 63 elements on cards (only 63 elements had been

Dmitry Mendeleyev devised the forerunner to today's periodic table. Initially a poor student, he eventually graduated from college at the top of his class.

Mendeleyev was 35 years old when he published his "Periodic Table of the Elements." This charcoal drawing, done by his wife, shows him in his later years, working in his laboratory. Part of his periodic table can be seen in the background of this picture.

Mendeleyev's early "Periodic Table" adorns the wall of the school where he worked in St. Petersburg, Russia. Mendeleyev's original table contained the 63 elements known at that time. He correctly predicted that the gaps would be filled with elements that had yet to be discovered.

discovered by 1869, the year he developed the card game). He then placed the cards face up on a table and began moving them around. He put the elements into groups according to the information he had about each one and how one element compared with another. For example, the elements sodium and potassium are soft, shiny, and highly reactive metals. Mendeleyev placed the cards for these elements in a column. He noticed that the elements calcium and magnesium had properties similar to one another, so he placed them together in another column. He did this with other elements and then moved the columns around so that the columns with similarities were next to one another. He discovered that when he did this, he could see patterns emerging. As he examined the rows of the table, he noticed that the

pattern of properties periodically repeated itself. Thus, he called this classification system the "Periodic Table of the Elements."

Over a period of 20 years, Mendeleyev improved his classification system. There were some gaps in the table—missing cards. He predicted that elements yet to be discovered would fill these gaps. He was able to suggest some of the characteristic properties they would have. As scientists became more knowledgeable about the physics and chemistry of matter, they helped refine the table, and the missing elements were discovered. □

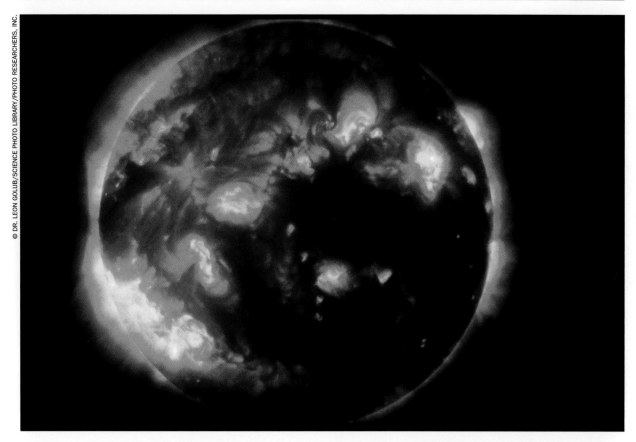

The periodic table is the "list of ingredients" for our entire universe. Most of the elements were formed in nuclear reactions, which took place inside stars or exploding stars called super nova. Some of these nuclear reactions continue to take place inside our sun (shown in this X-ray photograph), which releases energy when the element hydrogen undergoes fusion and is converted to the element helium.

QUESTION

The periodic table was not the work of one person. As with most discoveries, evidence was collected over many years and scientists in many different countries were involved. Use the Internet and other resources to find out about the most famous scientists involved in developing the periodic table.

22
Combining Elements

What is going on here? Is a chemical reaction taking place?
What are the reactants and products of this reaction?

INTRODUCTION

In the previous lesson, you discovered that elements can be classified into groups on the basis of their characteristic properties. In Inquiry 22.1, you will return to this theme and attempt to classify elements into two major groups. Your classification will then be used as a springboard to investigate the chemical properties of one of these groups in more detail. In Inquiry 22.2, you will investigate how two elements from the two groups you have identified react to make a compound. You will compare some of the properties of the reactants and products of the reaction and use a simple word equation to describe the reaction that has taken place.

OBJECTIVES FOR THIS LESSON

Examine the properties of four elements.

Place the four elements into two major groups.

Identify these groups on the periodic table.

Make a compound from elements in these two groups.

Construct a simple chemical equation for the reaction that has taken place.

Discuss the differences between reactants and products.

Getting Started

1. In Lesson 21, you grouped elements according to their properties. Your teacher will review some of these groups. Be prepared to contribute the name of a group you identified.

2. Imagine you have to split the elements you investigated into two groupings. Discuss the following questions with the other members of your group:

A. How would you select the groupings?

B. What properties (criteria) would you use to decide which elements go into which groupings? (The best groupings may use more than one property as criteria.)

C. What names would you give each grouping?

D. What are some elements you would put into each grouping?

3. Write your ideas in your science notebook.

SAFETY TIP

Wear your safety goggles at all times.

MATERIALS FOR LESSON 22

For you

1 copy of Student Sheet 22.1: Splitting the Periodic Table
1 copy of Student Sheet 22.2: Reacting Two Elements
1 pair of safety goggles

For you and your lab partner

2 test tubes
1 250-mL beaker
1 pair of scissors
1 index card
1 piece of steel wool
1 metric ruler
  Masking tape

For your group

1 bolt
1 cylinder
1 lump of yellow solid
1 lump of black solid

Inquiry 22.1
Splitting the Periodic Table

PROCEDURE

1. One student from your group should collect a plastic box containing the materials.

2. Check the contents of the plastic box against the materials list. (The plastic box does not contain the steel wool. You will collect that later.)

3. Take out the bolt, the cylinder, and the yellow and black samples. These are all elements. Examine them closely. Your teacher will ask you to identify them.

4. Sort these elements into the two groupings you identified in "Getting Started." If they do not fit easily into the two groupings, try changing the criteria you used to select the groupings. If necessary, decide on a new name for each grouping. Construct a table in your notebook that compares the properties of the elements in the two groupings. Compare as many different properties as you can. Use the information you collected about these elements in Student Sheet 21.1a (Table 1) to help you.

5. Your teacher will discuss the groupings you selected and choose two of the groupings to conduct a class brainstorming session. Your teacher will record the properties of each group on a Venn diagram. At the end of the brainstorming session, copy the completed Venn diagram into your notebook.

6. Label the Venn diagram on Student Sheet 22.1 with the names of the two groups. Try to place the elements you have encountered (both in the lessons and in your own experience) into one of the groups. If any elements seem to have intermediate properties (properties between both groups), place them in the area where the circles overlap.

7. Your teacher will ask you to give the names of elements and where you placed them on the Venn diagram.

8. Look at the periodic table in Student Sheet 21.1b. Is it possible to draw a line through the table that separates the nonmetals from the metals? Discuss this with your group and then use a pencil to draw the line.

Inquiry 22.2
Reacting Two Elements

PROCEDURE

1. If the index card does not already have holes in it, cut two round holes, each with a diameter that is slightly larger than the diameter of the test tubes (see Figure 22.1).

2. Put 150 mL of water into the beaker.

3. Use masking tape to affix the index card to the top of the beaker (see Figure 22.2).

4. Invert an empty test tube. Place the test tube through one of the holes in the card, making sure the open end of the test tube is resting on the bottom of the beaker (see Figure 22.3). You may need to tape the tube into place.

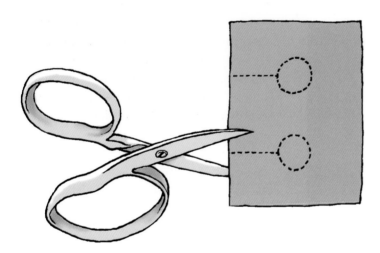

Figure 22.1 *Cut two holes in the index card. Each hole should have a diameter that is slightly larger than the diameter of the test tubes.*

Figure 22.2 *Use tape to affix the index card to the top of the beaker.*

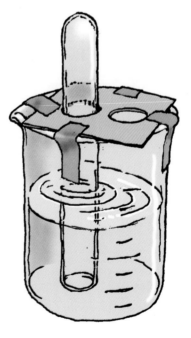

Figure 22.3 *Place an empty test tube through the index card, with the open end of the test tube resting on the bottom of the beaker.*

5. In Table 1 on Student Sheet 22.2, fill in the diagram of the empty test tube to show the water level in the test tube.

6. Collect a piece of damp steel wool from your teacher. The steel wool has been dipped in vinegar to clean off any grease or dirt. Steel wool is mainly iron with a little carbon added. For the purposes of this inquiry, it can be treated as if it is pure iron.

7. Quickly put the steel wool into the second test tube. Push it down to the bottom of the tube with a pencil.

8. Place the test tube through the other hole in the card, making sure the open end of the test tube is resting on the bottom of the beaker (see Figure 22.4).

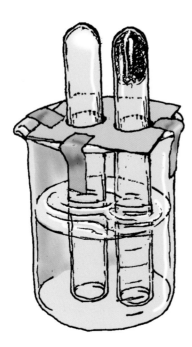

Figure 22.4 *The completed apparatus for Inquiry 22.2.*

9. Immediately show the water level by filling in the diagram in Table 1. Write a description of the damp steel wool in the third column of the table.

10. Watch the apparatus carefully. Do you notice anything happening in the tubes?

11. After about 15 minutes, look at the level of the water in each tube. Record your observations in the appropriate places in Table 1.

12. Describe the appearance of the steel wool.

13. Answer the following question on the student sheet: Has the water level changed in either tube? If so, can you explain the changes?

14. Air is about 20 percent oxygen. Keeping the tubes in position, remove the card and use the ruler to help you determine the approximate fraction of the length of the test tube that the water has moved. Answer these questions on Student Sheet 22.2: Has the water level changed in either tube? If so, can you explain the change? What can you conclude from your observations?

15. Clean the test tubes and the beaker. Make sure you remove the steel wool from the test tube and place it in the trash. Return the cleaned apparatus and the index card to the plastic box.

REFLECTING ON WHAT YOU'VE DONE

1. Discuss your results and compare them with those of other pairs.

2. Answer the following questions in Steps 4 through 8 on the student sheet: Why were two test tubes used in this experiment? What two elements have probably combined in the test tube containing the steel wool? Suggest a name for the new substance that has been formed. Name the reactants and the product(s) of the chemical reaction that has taken place. All chemical reactions have reactants and products and can be written as simple word equations. For example, you know that hydrogen combines with oxygen to form water. A simple word equation to describe this reaction is as follows:

hydrogen + oxygen → water

Write a word equation for the chemical reaction that took place in the test tube.

Synthesizing New Materials

Imagine what it would be like to invent a new substance. Many of the materials that we take for granted were invented. These materials are synthetic, which means they don't exist in nature. They have been made—or synthe-sized—from natural substances. Can you think of any examples of synthesized substances?

Probably the most well known group of syn-thetic substances is the plastics. Some of the early plastics were made from natural sub-stances, such as cellulose and latex, which are found in plants. The first really synthetic plas-tic was called Bakelite™, after its inventor, Leo Baekeland. In 1907, he found a way to control a chemical reaction between two existing sub-stances to produce a brittle, dark brown plastic that was, because of its insulating properties, used for making electrical fittings and house-hold items.

This vintage radio was made from Bakelite™, an early plastic.

Synthetic Materials Help Win a War

Many new synthetic plastics were first produced in bulk in the 1930s, just in time to play an important role in World War II. Here are some examples, which contributed to the victory of the Allies.

In 1931, Wallace Carothers, working at Dupont, invented a silklike synthetic plastic that was eventually called nylon. He made it by mixing together an acid and a solu-tion of another substance, diamine. Nylon, when used as a fiber, has many of the properties of silk but is stronger. In this picture, Carothers demonstrates another synthetic compound—a type of rubber.

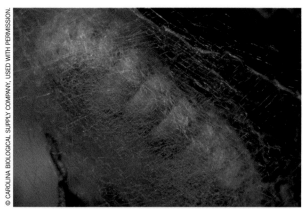

Silk, used to make parachutes, is produced by silk-worms. It was in short supply during World War II, but nylon came to the rescue!

Nylon was used in the manufacture of parachutes for aircrew and paratroopers.

Nylon and silk stockings were recycled to ensure adequate supplies.

When the Japanese army took over the rubber plantations in the Far East, rubber was in short supply. The tires on this army truck were made from a new plastic, sometimes called synthetic rubber.

Polyvinyl chloride (PVC) was used to insulate electrical wires inside aircraft.

Hundreds of synthetic plastics are in use today, all with different properties. They are used in products as varied as soda bottles, lenses, and artificial body parts. ☐

Polyacrylics (for example, Plexiglass™) were transparent and light and didn't shatter like glass—ideal properties when it came to aircraft manufacture.

Alchemy Into Chemistry

Since the dawn of civilization, chemical reactions have seemed magical. Certain rocks weep molten metal if put in a fire. Two substances mixed together burst into flames. Juice from a certain plant cures illness. It is no surprise, then, that early thinkers mixed magic with observation and experiment as they tried to understand the world.

The study of matter in ancient times began as alchemy, a mishmash of primitive chemistry, superstition, and showmanship. Alchemy had two main magical aims: to change common metals into gold and to find a medicine that would cure all ills, including old age. By the 1600s, alchemists were slowly learning that observation and experiment provided more useful information than magic and sorcery. They learned to make hypotheses, gather evidence, and form conclusions. The modern science of chemistry was born. ☐

Many books about alchemy were written. This medieval handwritten and hand-illuminated book was a forerunner to the modern chemistry text.

This woodcut shows an alchemist's lab in 16th-century Europe. The big pot in the middle of the furnace was used for purifying liquids by a process called distillation.

CORBIS/ARCHIVO ICONOGRAFICO, S.A.

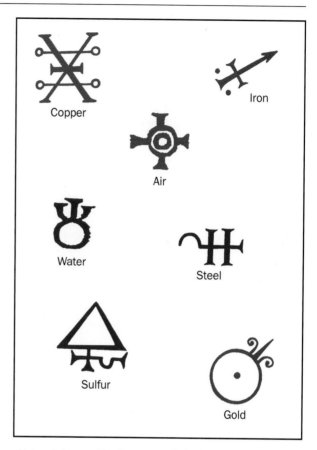

Copper

Iron

Air

Water

Steel

Sulfur

Gold

The Alchemist, *by the Italian artist Giovanni Stradano, depicts a wide variety of activities that may have taken place in an alchemist's laboratory. Versions of many of the apparatus being used can be found in a modern laboratory. Can you identify any of them?*

Alchemists used their own symbols that represented pure substances and mixtures. Can you identify which of these symbols represent elements, compounds, or mixtures?

COURTESY OF THE LIBRARY OF CONGRESS/ PHOTOASSIST, INC.

Scientist or alchemist? Isaac Newton was one of the greatest scientists the world has ever known. A physicist and mathematician, he lived and worked in the 1600s, just when real science was taking hold. Newton invented a form of calculus and discovered the laws that govern the motion of the planets. He was also fascinated by and learned a lot from alchemy.

LESSON 23
Chemical Reactions Involving Metals

The ancient Egyptians made part of Tutankhamen's throne from gold. Gold is valued for its scarcity. If gold is so scarce, why was it one of the first metals to be used?

INTRODUCTION

Earth's crust contains large amounts of many different metals, but pure chunks of metals are rarely found. Aluminum, for example, is the most common metal in Earth's crust, but it is never found naturally as a piece of aluminum metal. Aluminum exists naturally only combined with other elements, as aluminum compounds. You know that iron reacts with oxygen in the air. Would you expect to find a lot of pure iron metal lying around? Some metals, such as copper and gold, can be found as nuggets of pure metal. Why is it possible to find a rare metal, such as gold, in the form of pure nuggets, but not a common metal, such as magnesium? In this lesson, you will investigate the differences in the chemical properties of some metals. After this lesson, you may be able to answer some of these questions.

OBJECTIVES FOR THIS LESSON

Conduct an inquiry to compare how different metals react with acid.

Discuss how differences in the chemical properties of metals affect how they are extracted from their ores and used.

Design and conduct an experiment to compare how different metals corrode.

Getting Started

1. You know that metals have many properties in common. But do metals also have properties that differ from one another? Discuss with the members of your group how metals may differ in their properties. Be prepared to contribute your ideas to a class discussion.

2. Use the information you collected in Table 1 on Student Sheet 21.1a and your observations from Inquiry 22.2 to find out how one of the following metals reacts with oxygen in the air: copper, iron, magnesium, sodium, aluminum, zinc, calcium, and tin. Your teacher will assign a metal to your group.

3. Report on your findings. After your teacher lists your results, write the list in your science notebook. You will use this list later in the lesson.

MATERIALS FOR LESSON 23

For you

1 copy of Student Sheet 23.1: Comparing the Reaction of Different Metals With Acid

1 copy of Student Sheet 23.2: Investigating Corrosion

1 pair of safety goggles

For you and your lab partner

1 test tube rack

4 test tubes

1 lab scoop

1 bottle containing dilute hydrochloric acid

1 thermometer

1 metric ruler

For your group

1 jar of magnesium ribbon pieces

1 jar of granular zinc

1 jar of copper filings

1 jar of iron filings

1 plastic container

1 black marker

2 cotton balls

1 bottle of vegetable oil

5 labels

Access to boiled water

Access to anhydrous calcium chloride

4. After 5 minutes of group discussion, your teacher will conduct a brainstorming session of your ideas.

5. Use the class procedure to complete the first two columns of Table 1 on Student Sheet 23.2.

6. Your group will set up the apparatus to investigate the corrosion of one of the metals. Your teacher will assign a metal to your group. Write the name of the metal on the student sheet.

7. Using the labels and a marker, label each test tube with the numbers used in column 1 of Table 1. Also label the plastic container with the names of the members of your group and the name of the metal you are investigating.

8. As you set up each test tube, stand it in the plastic container. Place the container in the designated storage place (see Figure 23.2). You will look at the results of this experiment in about 4 days.

9. After about 4 days, record your observations in Table 1 on Student Sheet 23.2.

10. Discuss the results with the other members of your group and write in Table 1 your conclusions and any other notes you may have for each tube.

11. Your teacher will help you collect the results for all the metals from different groups. Summarize the class results in Table 2 on Student Sheet 23.2. Write your own conclusions for each metal.

12. Use the class results to answer the following questions on Student Sheet 23.2: Did all the metals corrode? Did all the metals corrode to the same extent? What is the relationship between the rate at which a metal corrodes in the presence of air and water and the rate at which it reacts with acid?

Figure 23.2 *Place the numbered tubes in the labeled container and put them in the place designated by your teacher.*

REFLECTING ON WHAT YOU'VE DONE

1. Review the results from both inquiries as well as the information you collected in "Getting Started." Do you recognize any similarities between the data obtained from the two inquiries? Be prepared to contribute your ideas about the chemical reactivity of metals to a class discussion.

2. On your student sheet, write a short paragraph about what you have found out about the chemical reactivity of metals (see Figure 23.3) and how this knowledge can be applied to choosing metals to do specific jobs (for example, use of copper to make water pipes).

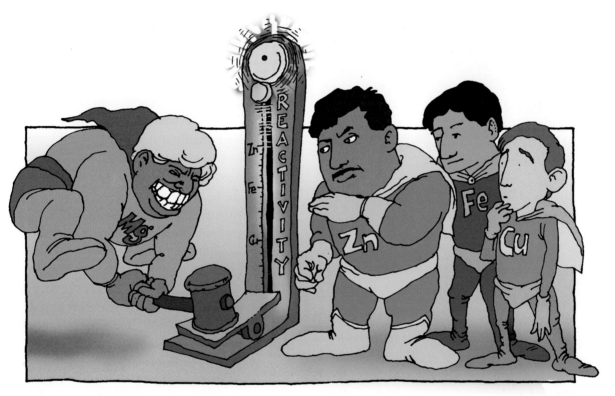

Figure 23.3 *Magnesium is the most reactive of the four metals.*

Reactivity and Free Metals

Copper is more reactive than gold. Sometimes it is found as nuggets as shown in this picture, but most copper is obtained by smelting copper ores. During smelting, the metal is extracted from the metal ore. The exact process depends on the type of ore. For example, if the ore is copper carbonate or copper oxide, smelting is achieved by roasting the ore with carbon, usually in the form of coke. A chemical reaction takes place that produces copper metal and carbon dioxide gas.

Gold is valued for its scarcity and for its lack of reactivity. Because it does not react with other elements, such as oxygen, it can be found in its pure form as nuggets. Metals that are not combined with other substances are called free metals. Gold's lack of reactivity also means that it stays shiny and does not corrode. This makes it ideal for use in jewelry and in electrical contacts (for example, the plugs on a computer cable).

Copper is a much more common metal than gold is, and sometimes nuggets of pure copper can be found. Copper can remain shiny for a long time, and it is also used to make jewelry. However, eventually it reacts with other elements, particularly oxygen in the air, and slowly corrodes (a process called tarnishing).

Iron is more reactive than copper. Because of its reactivity, iron is almost always found in Earth's crust combined with other elements. Rocks containing large amounts of iron compounds are called iron ore. Iron is extracted from these ores by a process called smelting. Chunks of natural iron are sometimes found, but these originate from outer space. Meteorites that fall to Earth are often composed mainly of iron. They can last thousands of years, but they also eventually corrode. □

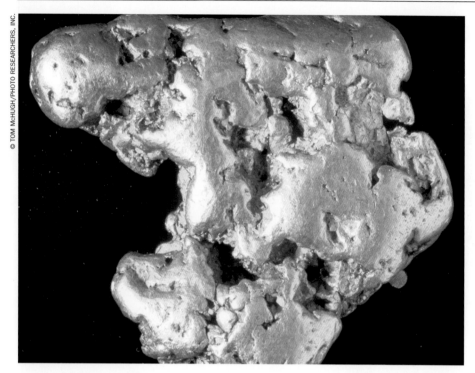

The low reactivity of gold explains why it can be found as metal nuggets. Most other metals exist as ores.

This giant iron meteorite is in the form of pure iron, which is rarely found on Earth. Why can iron exist in space but not for very long on the surface of Earth?

Making Metals by Mistake

Are you the sort of person who does things by trial and error? For example, if you get a new video game, do you put it in your machine and then try to play without reading the instruction manual? If so, you are in good company. Trial and error is a technique that has been used since prehistoric times. It is still used today because it works.

Consider the way people figured out how to make metals. Before about 5000 B.C., the only metals

This Mochica mask from northern Peru is made of copper. Although the Mochica civilization lasted for 1000 years, its smiths never mastered the production of iron. Why did early cultures make objects from less reactive metals such as copper, silver, and gold?

that people used came from nuggets of gold, silver, and copper. Nobody knew that metals were locked inside rocks. Nobody, that is, until someone probably made a very hot fire on top of some greenish rocks and saw molten copper trickling out.

Today, it is known that those greenish rocks contained copper combined with oxygen and other elements. Heating the rocks with a wood fire to several hundred degrees caused a chemical reaction. The rock turned to copper oxide, and the oxygen broke loose from the copper and combined with carbon from the wood. Carbon dioxide floated away. The copper stayed behind.

Of course, early people didn't know any of this. But that didn't stop them from experimenting. How much rock should be used? Which rocks work? Where are the rocks

found? How hot does the fire have to be? Does the type of wood matter? Does the phase of the moon make a difference? Would it help to add some dirt? If rocks can be changed to copper, can copper be turned into gold? After a few centuries of trials—and almost as many errors—people knew a lot about making copper and it became widely available.

The copper was not very hard. It could be made into pots and pans. It could be shaped into fancy jewelry. But it was too soft to make good tools or weapons. People needed tools and weapons, and more trial and error eventually led to the next big discovery.

In about 3800 B.C., a copper maker in the Middle East mixed tin ore with copper ore and heated them up. The resulting metal was very different from tin and from copper. This

Early armor, such as these Cypriot helmets, was made from alloys of less reactive metals. Bronze, an alloy of tin and copper, was used to make these helmets.

new metal, an alloy called bronze, was lighter in color than copper. It was also much harder than either copper or tin. This new alloy was used to make axes, spears, knives, armor, and other tools.

The secrets of making bronze soon spread to the Far East. By 1500 B.C., Chinese bronze makers had discovered, by trial and error, that the hardest bronze is exactly 85 percent copper and 15 percent tin. They had no idea

why this particular mixture was so hard. But by experimenting, watching carefully, and recording results, they found the best way to make bronze.

Iron was probably discovered by mistake, in much the same way as copper. However, iron ore requires a much hotter fire than that used to extract copper from ore. Can you think of the reason why the fire needs to be so hot?

Iron is much harder than bronze. Tools and weapons made of iron were much harder than those made from bronze. The techniques for extracting and improving the quality of iron were refined through trial and error, and the new technology spread quickly. The Iron Age had begun. ☐

QUESTION

Iron was discovered after copper and tin because it is more difficult to extract from its ore. What are the modern processes for extracting iron metal from its ores? Use information from the library and the Internet to find out more about these processes. Write a paragraph about the techniques involved, and illustrate your answer with a diagram.

Bronze is harder than either tin or copper—hard enough to use for armor in battle.

LESSON 24

Countering Corrosion

Why is it important to paint a steel ship?

COURTESY OF THE NATIONAL ARCHIVES

INTRODUCTION

Imagine you possessed the scientific knowledge to save the country tens of billions of dollars every year! If you could prevent a particular process from occurring, that much money could really be saved. The process is a chemical reaction that corrodes objects made of iron and steel. What is the common name given to this process? Can you identify the reactants and the products in this chemical reaction or the conditions needed for it to take place? How could you prevent it? In this lesson, you will investigate this process and find out the answers to these questions.

OBJECTIVES FOR THIS LESSON

Discuss ideas about the nature and the causes of rusting.

Design and conduct an inquiry to compare the effectiveness of different rust-prevention techniques.

Explain results in terms of the chemical reaction involved in the rusting process.

Getting Started

1. Your teacher will show you some objects. Participate in a class discussion about them.

2. Discuss the answers to the following questions with the other members of your group:

A. What is rust?

B. What conditions are required for rusting to take place?

C. Why is rusting a problem?

3. Think of as many methods of rust prevention as you can. After a few minutes, your teacher will conduct a brainstorming session on your ideas about preventing rust. Record these ideas in your science notebook.

MATERIALS FOR LESSON 24

For your group

- 1 black marker
- 2 petri dishes with lids
- 3 ungalvanized steel nails
- 1 ungalvanized painted steel nail
- 1 galvanized steel nail
- 1 stainless steel nail
- 1 magnesium ribbon
- 1 paper towel
- 2 labels

  Access to a jar of petroleum jelly

Inquiry 24.1
Can Rusting Be Stopped?

PROCEDURE

1. In this inquiry, you will work with the other members of your group to design an experiment to compare the effectiveness of different methods of rust prevention.

2. One member of your group should collect a plastic box containing the materials. Check its contents against the materials list.

3. Write the title of the inquiry in your notebook. Under the title, write a sentence or a short paragraph describing what you are trying to find out.

4. Discuss with the other members of your group how you could use the materials in the plastic box to design an experiment to compare the effect of corrosion on the following objects: a nail wrapped in magnesium, a stainless steel nail, a nail treated with paint, a galvanized (zinc-coated) nail, and a nail coated with petroleum jelly.

5. Come to an agreement on the design of your experiment and then set up the experiment. Using the labels in your plastic box, label your experiment with the names of the members of your group.

6. In your notebook, draw a labeled diagram showing how you set up the experiment. Below the diagram, write a short description of the procedure.

7. Design and draw your own results table. You will need to include items such as the appearance of the nails at the start of the experiment and at the end (which will be after at least 3–4 days). You may wish to score each nail for "rustiness."

8. Make sure that you check your apparatus every class period during the course of the experiment. It is your group's responsibility to make sure that the conditions the objects are exposed to remain constant.

9. After the designated time, record your results in the table and discuss your findings with the other members of your group.

10. A member of your group will be asked to report on some of your findings. Make sure you are ready to make such a report.

REFLECTING ON WHAT YOU'VE DONE

1. Discuss the class results with the other members of your group. Think about the answers to the following questions:

   A. Did all the rust-prevention techniques work?

   B. Were they equally effective?

   C. Why did some techniques work and others did not?

   D. How did the different techniques prevent the rusting reaction from taking place?

2. You will discuss your results with the rest of the class. After the discussion, write one sentence in your notebook, explaining what happened to each nail.

3. Write a paragraph summarizing everything you know about the process of rusting. Include a word equation for the process.

THE WORK NEVER ENDS

The Golden Gate Bridge is one of the world's great bridges. It spans 2.7 kilometers across the Golden Gate Strait at the end of San Francisco Bay. More than 1.5 billion cars have crossed over it. It contains 75 million kilograms of steel. It can withstand powerful tides, hurricane winds, and major earthquakes. But one thing could send it tumbling into the bay below: corrosion. The iron in steel combines with the oxygen in air to form iron oxide, or rust. Water and salt, which the bridge is constantly exposed to, greatly speed up rust formation. To keep the mighty bridge from crumbling apart, maintenance crews must constantly battle rust.

Preventing Rust

Dry steel rusts very, very slowly. But wet steel rusts very quickly. If steel is in contact with saltwater, it rusts even faster. Paint prevents rust by keeping oxygen, water, and salt away from the steel surface.

Applying the Paint

A painter puts down a primer coat. Primer sticks to the metal, but it isn't that tough or waterproof. So after the primer dries, the painter puts on two protective top coats of paint that keep out air and water.

The Golden Gate Bridge (San Francisco, California) is an example of steel used in close proximity to saltwater.

Touching Up

Whenever rust spots appear on the bridge, maintenance crews go to work scraping off the rust and worn paint. Metal workers then cut out and replace any corroded metal.

Repainting

Although it is called "Golden," the Golden Gate Bridge has always been painted International Orange. The bridge was first painted in 1937, the year it opened. Between 1965 and 1995, the entire bridge was repainted. Bit by bit, all of the old paint was scraped off and a new, tougher acrylic formula was put on. But even the new paint can break down in spots. Maintenance crews constantly inspect the bridge and touch up any rusted areas. ☐

QUESTION

How do car or bicycle manufacturers stop or reduce rusting? Draw a simple sketch of either a car or a bike and label all the different methods of rust prevention you can identify.

CORBIS/ROGER RESSMEYER

Paint is applied to combat the rust problem. Paint prevents the iron in the steel from coming into contact with water and oxygen, the other reactants in the rusting equation.

Mass and Chemical Reactions

INTRODUCTION

In this lesson, you will continue to investigate what happens to the mass of matter when it undergoes change. What rules apply to phase change and to dissolving? Can the same rules be applied to chemical reactions? For example, what do you think happens to the mass of a candle when it is burned? What happens to the mass of a nail when it rusts? What do you think happens to the total mass of matter in a chemical reaction when one of the products is a gas (for example, when you reacted magnesium with acid)? Is the mass of the reactants of these chemical reactions the same as the mass of the products? In Inquiry 25.1, you will investigate mass changes in a chemical reaction. You will measure mass before and after adding half an effervescent tablet to a beaker of water. You will then perform the same experiment inside a sealed bottle. You will be asked to interpret any changes in mass that take place in both experiments and to decide whether the law of conservation of mass can be applied to chemical reactions.

In this lesson, you will study what happens to the mass of reactants and products in this chemical reaction.

© T.J. FLORIAN/RAINBOW

OBJECTIVES FOR THIS LESSON

Conduct an inquiry to compare the mass of the reactants and the mass of the products in the chemical reaction that takes place when an effervescent tablet is added to water in both open and closed containers.

Determine whether the law of conservation of mass can be applied to chemical reactions.

Getting Started

1. Your teacher will conduct a review of Lessons 8 and 14, which discussed the conservation of mass during phase change and dissolving. After the review, write in your science notebook your own definition of the law of conservation of mass.

2. Discuss with your partner whether the law of conservation of mass can be applied to chemical reactions. Think about a chemical reaction you have observed. The following are some questions you should consider during your discussion:

A. What were the reactants and the products of the reaction?

B. Were they all the same phase of matter? Do you think this affects the mass of the matter?

C. You observed a burning candle in Lesson 1. What do you think happened to the mass of matter in that chemical reaction?

3. Your teacher will ask you about some of your ideas. While you are doing Inquiry 25.1, think about the points raised during this discussion and how your ideas change in response to the experimental evidence.

MATERIALS FOR LESSON 25

For you
- 1 copy of Student Sheet 25.1: Measuring Mass in a Chemical Reaction
- 1 copy of Student Sheet 25: Review for Compounds, Elements, and Chemical Reactions
- 1 pair of safety goggles

For you and your lab partner
- 1 250-mL beaker
- 1 effervescent tablet
- 1 paper towel
- 1 clear plastic soda bottle with a screw cap
  Access to an electronic balance
  Access to water

The Mass of Matter

Matter may change from a solid to a liquid. Elements may react together to form compounds. What happens to the mass of matter in a bowl of water when it is left to stand in the hot sun? What happens to the mass of matter in a piece of paper when it is burned? Sometimes in situations like this it seems as if matter is disappearing. But the disappearance of matter is an illusion.

Matter may change from one form into another. For example, when the water in the bowl absorbs energy from the sun and evaporates, it becomes water vapor in the atmosphere. The piece of paper gives off heat and light energy as it burns, and the matter in it is converted into carbon dioxide, water vapor, and other gases that escape into the atmosphere. Some of the mass will remain behind as ash. In both cases, the matter changes its form, but its total mass stays the same. The same mass of each element is present before

Antoine and Marie-Anne Lavoisier worked together on experiments that led to the law of conservation of mass.

and after the change. Matter is neither created nor destroyed during these changes.

It took early scientists hundreds of years of scientific study before the law of conservation of mass became accepted. For a long time, scientists had suspected that matter could not be created or destroyed, but nobody had performed an experiment that proved it.

During the late 18th century, French chemist Antoine Lavoisier and his wife Marie-Anne conducted several experiments that demonstrated the conservation of mass. Antoine was famous for his accurate observations and insistence on careful measurements. He used accurate balances that could measure very small changes in mass during his experiments.

Many of the Lavoisiers' experiments were conducted in sealed glass containers from which matter could not escape or enter. For

Antoine Lavoisier (1743–1794) was one of the founders of modern chemistry.

example, in one experiment, Antoine put fruit into a sealed container, measured its mass, and then left it in a warm place for a few days. The fruit rotted and changed into a putrid mess. Gas was released from the decomposing fruit and droplets of water formed on the glass, but nothing escaped from the container. Lots of changes had taken place, but the mass of the sealed container and the rotten fruit was equal to the mass measured at the beginning of the experiment.

In other experiments, Antoine heated elements in enclosed containers with air inside them. He discovered that new substances were formed but that the container and its contents had the same mass as they did before heating. When he measured the mass of the new solid substances he had made, he discovered that they were heavier than the original elements he heated. In this way, he determined that they must have gained their mass from the air. On the basis of these experiments, he also concluded that air contained several gases,

one of which reacted with the elements in the experiment. He called this gas oxygen (which had previously been discovered and described—but not named—by Carl Wilhelm Scheele and by Joseph Priestley).

In 1789, Antoine wrote the best textbook on chemistry the world had seen. In it, he introduced a new scientific law that he called the law of conservation of mass. This law stated that in any closed system (as small as a sealed container or as big as the whole universe!) the total mass remains the same, regardless of what changes take place inside. ☐

QUESTION

Imagine you are Antoine Lavoisier. How could you design an experiment to investigate what happens to the total mass of matter when a caterpillar eats a leaf? Draw a picture of the apparatus you would use and write a short description of the procedure you would follow. Remember that Antoine Lavoisier did not have electronic balances.

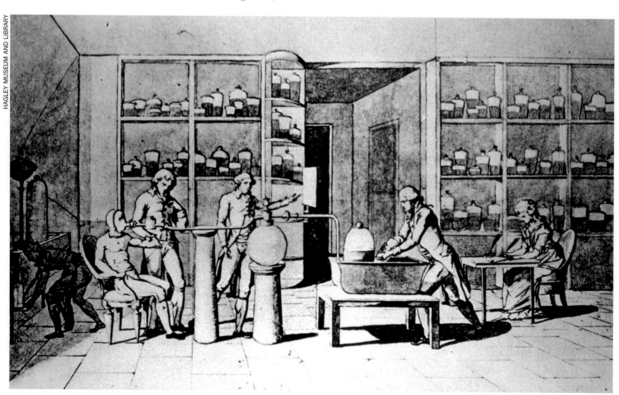

Antoine Lavoisier was particularly interested in the chemistry of gases. This picture shows him working with other scientists on an investigation of the gases exchanged during breathing.

26

End-of-Module Assessment

In this lesson, you will conduct an inquiry that requires you to carefully follow instructions. You will also have to make and record accurate measurements and observations.

INTRODUCTION

This lesson is designed to assess how much you have learned while working on the module *Properties of Matter.* The assessment consists of two parts: a performance assessment (Inquiry 26.1) and a written assessment.

OBJECTIVES FOR THIS LESSON

Use your knowledge and skills to complete an assessment of what you have learned during the module *Properties of Matter.*

Getting Started

1. Your teacher will assign a set of materials and a balance to you and your lab partner. Make sure you have all the apparatus listed in the materials list.

2. You may refer to your Student Guide and science notebook for Inquiry 26.1. You may talk to your lab partner, but do not share information or results with other pairs of students. Answer questions on your own.

3. Your teacher will explain when and how to do the written assessment.

MATERIALS FOR LESSON 26

For you

- 1 copy of Student Sheet 26.1: Performance Assessment
- 1 copy of Student Sheet 26: Written Assessment
- 1 pair of safety goggles

For you and your lab partner

- 1 jar of solid A
- 1 bottle of clear solution C
- 1 250-mL beaker
- 1 250-mL beaker containing about 50 mL of water
- 1 lab scoop
- 3 test tubes
- 1 metric ruler
- 1 black permanent marker
- 3 labels
  Access to an electronic balance

Inquiry 26.1
Performance Assessment

PROCEDURE

1. You have 35 minutes to complete this part of the assessment.

2. In this inquiry, you need to measure mass accurately. Be careful not to spill solids or liquids after you have measured their mass. If you do, start the experiment again. If you make a mistake or spill anything, you may request replacement items from your teacher.

3. Use the black permanent marker and labels to label the three test tubes (A, B, and C) in the beaker.

4. Put one level lab scoop of solid A into test tube A (see Figure 26.1). Stand the test tube in the beaker.

5. Pour water to a depth of about 4 cm into test tube B. Use the ruler to measure the depth. Stand the test tube in the beaker.

6. Pour the clear solution from the bottle labeled C, to a depth of about 4 cm in test tube C. Stand the test tube in the beaker.

Figure 26.1 *Put one lab scoop of solid A into test tube A.*

SAFETY TIP

Wear your safety goggles at all times during the inquiry.

7. Carry the beaker and test tubes to the balance.

8. Measure the mass of the apparatus (see Figure 26.2). Record your result in Table 1 (under "Before Mixing Contents of Tube A and Tube B") on Student Sheet 26.1.

9. Remove the beaker and test tubes from the balance. Return to your place.

10. *Without spilling any,* pour the water from test tube B into test tube A (see Figure 26.3). Return test tube B to the beaker.

Figure 26.2 *Measure the mass of the beaker and the three tubes on the balance.*

Figure 26.3 *Without spilling any, add the water from test tube B to test tube A.*

11. Gently shake test tube A from side to side as shown in Figure 26.4. It is very important that you do not place your fingers or thumb over the top of the test tube. Be very careful not to spill any of the liquid. Continue to shake the tube until all the blue crystals dissolve.

12. Return the test tube to the beaker.

13. Remeasure the mass of the beaker and test tubes. Record the mass in Table 1 (under "After Mixing Contents of Tube A and Tube B") on the student sheet. Calculate any changes in mass and enter your answer in the appropriate place on the table.

14. Look carefully at the mixture in the test tube. Answer the following question in Step 2 on Student Sheet 26.1: What are three properties of solid A?

15. Carefully pour the contents of test tube C into test tube A. Again, be sure not to spill anything. Return the test tubes to the beaker.

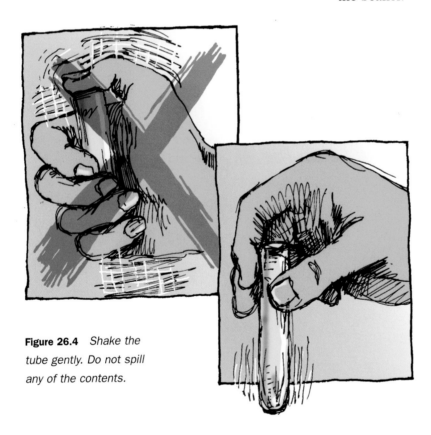

Figure 26.4 *Shake the tube gently. Do not spill any of the contents.*

16. Answer the following questions in Step 3 on the student sheet: What did you observe when you mixed the contents of test tube A and test tube C? What evidence was there that a chemical reaction took place?

17. Return to the balance and remeasure the mass of your apparatus. Record the mass in Table 1 (under "After Mixing Contents of Tube A and Tube C") on the student sheet. Calculate any changes in mass and enter your answer in the appropriate place on the table.

18. Answer the following questions in Step 4 on the student sheet: Was there any change in the mass of the apparatus when you made the solution? Was there any change in the mass after you mixed the two solutions together? Explain these results.

19. Dispose of the contents of your test tubes and rinse them with tap water.

20. Return to your place and check your answers.

Glossary

alchemy: An early form of chemical science and philosophy.

alloy: A mixture or solid solution of two metals or a metal and a nonmetal.

boiling: The process by which a liquid turns into a gas at its boiling point.

boiling point: The temperature at which a liquid turns into a gas. Boiling points depend on air pressure. Boiling points of substances are usually given for standard air pressure (1 atmosphere).

burning: A rapid chemical reaction between a substance and a gas that produces heat and light. Most burning or combustion takes place in the air and has oxygen as one of its reactants.

Celsius: A temperature scale with the melting point of ice at 0 degrees and the boiling point of water at 100 degrees. The divisions on the Celsius scale are the same as those on the Kelvin scale. *See also* **Kelvin.**

characteristic property: An attribute that can be used to help identify a substance. A characteristic property is not affected by the amount or shape of a substance.

chemical property: A characteristic of a substance that involves chemical reactions.

chemical reaction: Any change that involves the formation of a new substance. A chemical reaction has reactants and products.

chromatography: A process used to separate different solutes from a solution by passing them through a medium. In paper chromatography, the medium is paper.

composite: A material made from two or more substances: for example, resin and glass fibers in fiberglass.

compound: A pure substance consisting of two or more elements combined. For example, sodium chloride consists of the elements sodium and chlorine.

condensation: The process by which a gas turns into a liquid.

conductor: A substance that allows electricity and/or heat to pass through it.

convection current: Movement of a gas, liquid, or plastic solid caused by variations in density that result from uneven heating of matter.

corrosion: A chemical reaction, usually between a metal and the air. For example, iron reacts with the oxygen in air, which is called rusting.

density: The mass of a known volume of a substance. It is usually measured in grams per cubic centimeter (g/cm^3).

dissolving: The process that takes place when a solvent is mixed with a solute to make a solution. For example, when sodium chloride is mixed with water, it dissolves to form a solution of sodium chloride in water.

distillation: The process of evaporating a solution and then condensing the various fractions back into a liquid in order to separate them.

electrolysis: The process by which some liquid compounds or some compounds in solution are split into their constituent parts by passing electricity through them.

element: A substance that cannot be broken down into other substances by chemical or physical means (except by nuclear reaction).

evaporate: To change from a liquid to a gas at or below the boiling point.

expansion: The increase in the volume of matter that occurs when matter is heated.

Fahrenheit: A temperature scale with the melting point of ice at 32 degrees and the boiling point of water at 212 degrees. *See also* **Celsius; Kelvin.**

filtration: The process of separating a solid and a liquid by passing a mixture of the two through a mesh (usually a filter paper). The liquid, which passes through the filter paper, is called the filtrate. The solid, which remains on the filter paper, is called the residue.

freeze: The change in state in which a liquid turns into a solid.

gas: A state or phase of matter in which a substance has no definite shape or volume. Oxygen is an example of a gas.

gram: A metric unit used to measure mass. *See also* **density.**

immiscible: A term used to describe liquids that are unable to dissolve in one another. *See also* **miscible.**

Kelvin: A temperature scale with the lowest possible temperature at the zero point, which is called absolute zero. On the Kelvin scale, ice melts at 273 K. *See also* **Celsius.**

liquid: A state or phase of matter in which a substance has a definite volume but no definite shape. Liquids take the shape of the part of the container they occupy.

magnetic: A substance that is attracted to a magnet.

mass: A measure of the amount of matter in an object. Mass is measured in grams or kilograms.

material: The substance from which something is made.

matter: Substances that make up the universe. All matter has mass and volume.

melting: The phase change in which a solid turns into a liquid.

melting point: The temperature at which a solid turns into a liquid. The melting point of a substance is the same temperature as its freezing point. Melting points of substances are altered by changes in pressure and are usually given for standard air pressure (1 atmosphere).

metals: A group of elements that are usually hard solids and that have the following common characteristic properties: shiny appearance, good conductivity, and malleability. *See also* **nonmetals.**

miscible: A term used to describe liquids that are able to dissolve in one another. *See also* **immiscible.**

mixture: Two or more elements or compounds that are mixed together but are not chemically combined.

nonmetals: A group of elements with characteristic properties that are different from the characteristic properties of metals. Nonmetals are nonconductive, brittle, and dull in appearance. *See also* **metals.**

phase or **state:** Solids, liquids, and gases are the three phases or states of matter. For example, in a mixture of ice and water, ice is the solid phase and water is the liquid phase. Water in the gaseous phase is called water vapor or steam.

physical properties: All the characteristic properties of a substance except those that determine how it behaves in a chemical reaction.

product: A substance formed by a chemical reaction.

pure substance: Either an element or a compound.

reactant: The starting substances in a chemical reaction.

reactivity: The readiness of a substance to react chemically.

respiration: A series of chemical reactions that take place in the cells of organisms during which energy used for life processes is released.

saturated solution: A solution that will not dissolve any more solute at a given temperature or pressure. For example, if copper (II) sulfate is added to a test tube of saturated solution of copper (II) sulfate, the crystals will remain undissolved at the bottom of the test tube.

sedimentation: The process by which a solid settles out from a solid/liquid mixture. The solid that collects below the liquid is called a sediment.

smelting: The process by which a metal is extracted from ore. Smelting involves heating the ore, usually with a source of carbon.

solid: A phase or state of matter in which a substance has definite shape and volume.

solubility: The amount of solute that will dissolve in a solvent at a given temperature and pressure.

solute: The substance that dissolves in a solvent. Solutes may be solids, liquids, or gases.

solution: A homogeneous mixture of a solvent and one or more solutes.

solvent: The substance in a solution that dissolves the solute.

synthesis reaction: A chemical reaction in which the reactants are elements. A compound is made of the two (or more) elements.

temperature: The measurement of how hot an object is. Temperature is measured using a temperature scale (*see* **Celsius; Fahrenheit; Kelvin**). Temperature should not be confused with heat (total energy content), which is measured in joules.

thermal decomposition: A chemical reaction in which a compound is decomposed by heating.

volume: The amount of space occupied by a sample of matter. Volume is measured in liters (L) and milliliters (mL) as well as in cubic centimeters (cm^3) and cubic meters (m^3).

weight: A measure of the force of gravity. Like all forces, weight is measured in newtons (N).

Index

Photo Credits

PART 1: CHARACTERISTIC PROPERTIES OF MATTER
xviii-1 © David Marsland 2 National Oceanic and Atmospheric Administration (NOAA) Photo Library/Department of Commerce 10 CORBIS/Penny Tweedie 11 (top and bottom) National Aeronautics and Space Administration (NASA) 14 CORBIS/Digital Stock 22 Courtesy of the Smithsonian Institution, Neg. #56119 24 © John S. Lough/Visuals Unlimited 28 (top) CORBIS/Bettmann (bottom) AP/WIDE WORLD PHOTOS 29 USCG photo by Brandon Brewer, Atlantic Area Public Affairs 30 Science VU/Visuals Unlimited 34 (top) © Jeff Greenberg/Visuals Unlimited (bottom) Courtesy of the National Archives/PhotoAssist, Inc. 35 (top) © Dave B. Fleetham/Visuals Unlimited (bottom) NASA 36 (top) Courtesy of NASA/PhotoAssist, Inc. (bottom) © Tom J. Ulrich/Visuals Unlimited 37 © John Blaustein/Woodfin Camp & Associates 38 © Bob Daemmrich/Stock, Boston/PNI 43 (top) GLA Agricultural Electronics (bottom) CORBIS/Lowell Georgia 44 Courtesy of the Library of Congress 45 (left) Courtesy of the Library of Congress (center) Courtesy of Uppsala University (right) Courtesy of the National Archives/PhotoAssist, Inc. 46–47 © Ferne Saltzman/Albuquerque International Balloon Fiesta 47 Courtesy of San Diego Aerospace Museum 49 Image courtesy of NASA/Goddard Space Flight Center and Orbital Imaging Corporation (ORBIMAGE) 50 (top) © Harold Simon/Tom Stack & Associates (right) CORBIS/Yann Arthus-Bertrand (bottom) NOAA Photo Library/U.S. Department of Commerce 51 Anne B. Keiser 53 Photo courtesy Alyeska Pipeline Service Company 54 © Ken M. Johns/Photo Researchers, Inc. 56 © Hank Morgan/Rainbow 61 (left) CORBIS/Jonathan Blair (right) © Charles D. Winters/Photo Researchers, Inc. 62 (top) © TASS/Sovfoto/Eastfoto/PNI (bottom) © Alfred Pasieka/Science Photo Library/Photo Researchers, Inc. 63 (left) © Biophoto Associates/

Science Source/Photo Researchers, Inc. (right) © Todd Buchanan 64 Courtesy of the Library of Congress/PhotoAssist, Inc. 68 (left) Historic VU/Visuals Unlimited (right) Photo courtesy of Pennsylvania Historical & Museum Commission, Drake Well Museum, Titusville, PA 69 (left) © Bill Strode/Woodfin Camp & Associates (right) © Alon Reininger/Contact Press Images/PNI 71 Ebrie goldcasters making pendants by lost wax method; cleaning wax with crushed leaf juice; Anna village, Cote d'Ivoire, Photograph by Eliot Elisofon, 1972, Image no. H 2 Ebr 4, National Museum of African Art 72 Ebrie goldcasters making pendants by lost wax method, Anna village, Cote d'Ivoire, Photograph by Eliot Elisofon, 1972, Image no. H 2 Ebr 13, National Museum of African Art 73 (top) Figure of a king (oba), 19th century, Edo peoples, Benin Kingdom, Nigeria, Cooper alloy, Gift of Joseph H. Hirshhorn to the Smithsonian Institution in 1966, 85-19-12, Photograph by Franko Khoury, National Museum of African Art (bottom) Photo compliments of Investment Casting Institute, 8150 N. Central Expressway, Suite M1008, Dallas, TX 75206 74 © Bernhard Edmaier/Science Photo Library/Photo Researchers, Inc. 75 © David Marsland 78 © Paul Shambroom/Photo Researchers, Inc. 81 © 1988 Steve Finberg 83 Science Museum/Science & Society Picture Library

PART 2: MIXTURES AND SOLUTIONS 84-85 © Terry G. McCrea/Smithsonian Institution 86 © Henry Horestein/Stock, Boston/PNI 88 CORBIS/Kevin R. Morris 94 (top, bottom) © David Marsland 96 AP/WIDE WORLD PHOTOS 98 CORBIS/Philip Gould 99 © Carolina Biological Supply Company, used with permission 102 © David Marsland 103 (top) Photo by Brian O'Keefe (bottom) Photo courtesy of U.S. Navy Blue Angels. The Blue Angels and the U.S. Navy do not endorse this product. 104 © Archive Photos/PNI 105 (left) CORBIS/Hulton-Deutsch Collection (right) AP/WIDE WORLD PHOTOS 106 © Eastcott/Momatiuk/Woodfin Camp &

Associates **110 (left)** © Dan McCoy/Rainbow **(right)** © Bill Bachmann/Photo Researchers, Inc. **111 (top left)** © Eastcott/Momatiuk/Woodfin Camp & Associates **(top right)** © Mike Yamashita/Woodfin Camp/PNI **(bottom)** © Gary Milburn/Tom Stack & Associates **112** © Georg Gerster/Photo Researchers, Inc. **116** Anne Williams/NSRC **122** © Tom Stack/Tom Stack & Associates **126** © Dan McCoy/Rainbow **127** © Sidney Moulds/Science Photo Library/Photo Researchers, Inc. **128** © Georg Gerster/Photo Researchers, Inc. **129 (top)** Courtesy of the Library of Congress **(bottom)** Photo courtesy of US Bureau of Reclamation **130** © Jose Azel/Aurora/PNI **134** U.S. Department of Energy **136** © Rosenfeld Images Ltd./Science Photo Library/Photo Researchers, Inc. **137 (top)** © David Marsland **(bottom)** CORBIS/ Philadelphia Museum of Art **138** Courtesy of the National Archives **139** © Mike Yamashita/Woodfin Camp & Associates **140** Courtesy of Carolina Biological Supply Company **146** Courtesy of Federal Bureau of Investigation **147 (left, right)** Courtesy of Federal Bureau of Investigation **148** CORBIS/Bryn Colton; Assignments Photogra **150** Byron Augustin/ DDB Stock Photo **154 (top, bottom)** © David Marsland **(center)** © Bernard Boutrit/Woodfin Camp & Associates **158** CORBIS/Asian Art & Archaeology, Inc. **159 (left, right)** © Kenji Mishina **160 (top, bottom)** Courtesy of the Library of Congress **162** © Terry G. McCrea/Smithsonian Institution **165 (top)** CORBIS/PEMCO—Webster & Stevens Collection; Museum of History & Industry, Seattle **(bottom)** Courtesy of the Library of Congress **166** Cynthia Brito/DDB Stock Photo **167 (top)** © Mike Yamashita/ Woodfin Camp/PNI **(bottom)** Courtesy of the Library of Congress/© 1942 Winter & Pond

PART 3: COMPOUNDS, ELEMENTS, AND CHEMICAL REACTIONS 168-169 © Terry G. McCrea/Smithsonian Institution **170** NASA **176** © Peter Skinner/Photo Researchers, Inc. **177** © Joel Rogers/AllStock/PNI

178 (top) © David Marsland **(bottom)** © Chris Rogers/Rainbow **181 (top, bottom)** CORBIS/ Bettmann-UPI **182 (top)** © Mary Evans Picture Library/Photo Researchers, Inc. **(bottom)** New York Times Pictures **183 (left)** CORBIS/James L. Amos **(right)** © Alcoa, Inc. **184 (top)** © Bob Daemmrich/ Stock, Boston/PNI **(bottom)** © Alcoa, Inc. **185 (middle, right)** © Alcoa, Inc. **186** © Grazia Neri/Woodfin Camp & Associates **189 (left)** CORBIS/The Purcell Team **(right)** CORBIS/Christine Osborne **190 (left)** U.S. Dept. of Energy/Photo Researchers, Inc. **(right)** Courtesy of the National Archives **191 (left)** NASA **(right)** Photo copyright Joel Silverstein **195 (top)** © Science Photo Library/Photo Researchers, Inc. **(bottom)** Smithsonian Institution Libraries **196** CORBIS/Steve Raymer **197** © Dr. Leon Golub/Science Photo Library/Photo Researchers, Inc. **198** © Spencer Swanger/Tom Stack & Associates **204 (top)** CORBIS/Digital Stock **(bottom left)** Hagley Museum and Library **(bottom right)** © Carolina Biological Supply Company, used with permission **205 (top left)** Courtesy of the National Archives **(left center, bottom, top right)** FDR Library **(bottom right)** Courtesy of the Library of Congress **206 (top)** © Jean-Loup Charmet/Science Photo Library/Photo Researchers, Inc. **(bottom)** Dover Publications, Inc. **207 (top)** CORBIS/Archivo Iconografico, S.A. **(bottom)** Courtesy of the Library of Congress/PhotoAssist, Inc. **208** CORBIS/Digital Stock **214** Ken Hammond/USDA **215 (top)** © Tom McHugh/Photo Researchers, Inc. **(bottom)** © Jonathan Blair/Woodfin Camp & Associates **216** © Robert Frerck/Woodfin Camp & Associates **217** © Jonathan Blair/Woodfin Camp & Associates **218** Courtesy of the National Archives **222** CORBIS/Digital Stock **223** CORBIS/Roger Ressmeyer **224** © T.J. Florian/Rainbow **228 (top)** CORBIS/ Bettmann **(bottom)** Archives Center, NMAH, Smithsonian Institution **229** Hagley Museum and Library **230** © Terry G. McCrea/Smithsonian Institution